# THE BUILDIM
# STONES OF CARDIFF

## . . . GEOLOGICAL TRAIL GUIDES

JOHN W. PERKINS

UNIVERSITY COLLEGE CARDIFF PRESS
1984

**British Library Cataloguing in Publication Data**
Perkins, John W.
   Building stones of Cardiff: geological
   trail guides.
   1. Masonry—History   2. Cardiff (South
   Glamorgan)—History
   I. Title
   693'.1'0942987      TH5321

ISBN   0 906449 77 4

*Illustrations by the author, except Figures 27 and 28 which are by Roy Pearce. The map on the inside rear cover is derived from an Institute of Geological Sciences draft map which was displayed at the National Museum in 1983.*

*First published in 1984 by University College Cardiff Press, P.O. Box 78, Cardiff, CF1 1XL, Wales, United Kingdom.*

Printed in Great Britain by
J. W. Arrowsmith Ltd., Bristol

# Contents

# Introduction

Cardiff has historically commanded the flood plain lowlands of the Rivers Taff, Ely and Rhymney, the low ground between the South Wales coalfield and the shore of the Bristol Channel. Its site is a classic one, the lowest bridging point of a river.

The city occupies a position fortified since Roman times, and, from the fourth fortress built by the Romans, one which has seen the use of local stone in its buildings. The earliest to be used were the river cobbles of Carboniferous and Old Red Sandstones, Blue Lias blocks from the Glamorgan cliffs, and a little imported golden Dundry Stone from south of Bristol. These materials were the best available from Roman times until the early nineteenth century, e.g. the medieval walls were built of Blue Lias, and by and large still enclosed the early nineteenth century town.

The great expansion of Cardiff in the mid- and late-nineteenth century came with its growth as a port for the coalfield to the north, through the development of canal and railway links and the enterprises of the Marquis of Bute in building the Cardiff docks. These developments widened the variety of local building stones available, increased the demand for them, and in particular gave access to the huge resources of Pennant Sandstones in the coalfield. Thus, Cardiff's central area is still partly that of a Victorian city, built in the time when stone was used for both public buildings and houses, a town from the era before brick was much used externally or large buildings were clad in concrete.

The rapid growth led to an upsurge in demand for local materials, favouring the grey Pennant Sandstone from the local coalfield, but also bringing in resources from further afield. The fashionable Bath Stone is the most obvious example, used in dressings as a foil to the sombre Pennant. Secondly, the growth of a large commercial city created a demand for special stones, of particular qualities or aesthetic appeal, e.g. the imposing white Portland Stone for major public buildings, while thirdly, the coal trade itself played an unexpected role. It was a one-sided trade, boats often returning to Cardiff in ballast with stones in the hold, thus bringing in a whole variety of

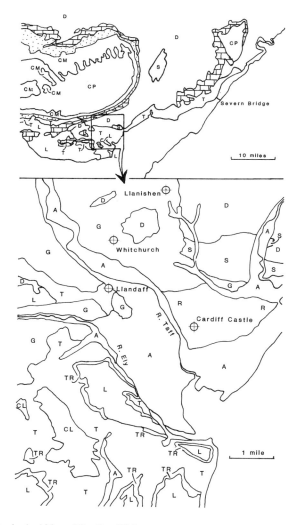

FIG. 1   Geological Map of the Cardiff Area.
Upper map: Generalised Solid Geology, S.E. Wales. Lower map: Generalised Solid and Drift Geology, City of Cardiff. R, Recent river gravels; A, Recent alluvium; G, Glacial gravels; L, Jurassic Lias; TR, Triassic, Rhaetic beds; T, Triassic marls; CP, Carboniferous, Pennant and barren Upper Coal Measures; CM Carboniferous, Coal Measures; dotted symbol, Carboniferous, Millstone Grit; CL and brick symbol, Carboniferous Limestone; D, Devonian, Old Red Sandstones; S, Silurian.

materials from all over Europe and the Mediterranean, stuff so ill-assorted that only the poorer houses were completely built of it but which was widely employed by local builders in decorative friezes, and in back lane and boundary walls. In 1856 the builders even retained an agent to negotiate ballast stone purchases with the Marquis of Bute's agent.

The ballast stones pose great problems for geological study. The rock type can be determined, but the source only if there is corroborating written evidence. Much of it came from Mediterranean countries and this is proved by the plant seeds which travelled with it. Forty-eight species of Mediterranean flora once flourished in Cardiff's docks! Identification is more difficult however when the stones come from North-West European ports, or areas with a similar geology or flora. Recourse must then be made to shipping records, which show innumerable cargoes of 'stones'. Some of these were undoubtedly ballast, but others were limestone for burning and many were igneous setts for street paving. These must not be confused with the ballast stones used in walling.

Many Victorian streets were paved with setts (cobble stones). Those which survive in Cardiff are mainly granite. Granite setts came into Cardiff from Fowey in Cornwall and probably also from Guernsey. The second most commonly used material was dolerite, and the main Welsh source of supply from the Ordovician Penmaenmawr intrusion west of Conway. Cobble stones taken up in recent redevelopment also show high-grade metamorphic rocks with garnets in them, indicating possible sources in Scotland, Norway or even the St. Lawrence region of Canada, vividly illustrating the problems of identification of sources.

A fourth factor enriching Cardiff's building stones was the fashion for stone cladding, for covering buildings with thin slabs of exotic igneous rocks and marbles, from even more world-wide origins. This fashion began in France and Belgium in the 1930s and is still important today.

Today as the capital city of Wales, Cardiff has developed a shopping centre and public buildings which are sufficient to attract many fine examples of British and foreign building stones. The city has become a major local resource for geological study. There are British sedimentary and igneous rocks, foreign marbles and lavas, stones from as far apart as Finland

and Uruguay, from Rome, from Ireland, from France and the United States of America. Among them are granites and sandstones, slate and travertine, syenites and breccias, fine fossils of algae and corals, of oysters and other shells. A geologist can study many aspects of his subject, many areas of the world and periods of earth history, all beautifully illustrated in the walls of Cardiff!

Geologists divide rocks into sedimentary, igneous and metamorphic types. Sedimentary rocks are laid down in rivers, seas and lakes or by ice and are generally layered (bedded). They vary greatly in grain size and colour and include sandstones, shales, mudstones, limestones, breccias and conglomerates. Certain sandstones and limestones are the most useful as building stones. If a sedimentary rock can be cut in any direction, independently of its natural joints, it is termed a freestone. This can be a very useful property for building purposes. Walls of sedimentary rock may also reveal fossils.

Igneous rocks are those formed from molten material, and they include those intruded below ground, of which granites, gabbros and dolerites are the most commonly used in buildings, and volcanic material ejected at the earth's surface. Being mainly ashes, cinders and lavas with many gas cavities, few volcanic materials find a use in building.

The third main group of rocks is that which has been altered by contact with a source of heat or by great pressure, the metamorphic rocks. Many decorative stones are derived from this group, e.g. all true marbles are produced by metamorphism of originally limestone deposits. Another metamorphosed material commonly found on shop fronts is serpentinite.

Most local buildings have walls of material originally laid down as sediments, quarried locally or in other parts of Britain. Cardiff also displays numerous intrusive rocks, mainly granites and dolerites, as well as occasional examples of extrusive igneous, i.e. volcanic, rocks. In shop frontages the range of stones used increases dramatically – examples of British and foreign igneous rocks are numerous, but there is also a wide range of marbles, some being highly polishable British limestones, but most are true metamorphosed marbles from abroad, derived from the alteration of original limestone deposits or serpentinites.

Geologists have become more aware of the value of building

stones as a source of study as the need to conserve natural exposures has become more urgent. However, it is a task full of pitfalls. The type of material can usually be determined, but the source of the stone may be difficult to ascertain. Today, many commonly used stones can come from a variety of places with similar geological histories. Without written records it may be impossible to identify the source, and to date there is no proper recording system which architects, contractors and shopfitters must use. In recent years stones from further afield than ever before have found their way into British buildings,

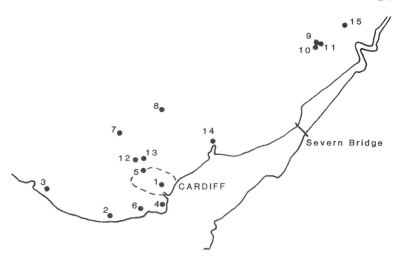

Fig. 2   Local Sources of Cardiff Building Stones.

| Recent | 1. River cobbles. |
| Jurassic | 2. Normal Blue Lias. |
| | 3. Marginal Lias, Sutton Stone. |
| Triassic | 4. Gypsum nodules. |
| | 5. Marginal Triassic, Radyr Stone. |
| | 6. Marginal Triassic, Cadoxton. |
| Carboniferous | 7. Pennant Sandstone, Pontypridd. |
| | 8.      ,,          ,,         Newbridge. |
| | 9.      ,,          ,,         Forest of Dean Grey. |
| | 10.    ,,          ,,         Forest of Dean Blue. |
| | 11.    ,,          ,,         Forest of Dean Mine Train. |
| | 12. Pentyrch limestone. |
| | 13. Creigiau limestone. |
| Devonian | 14. Newport Old Red Sandstone. |
| | 15. Red Wilderness or Forest of Dean Red Sandstone. |

FIG. 3   Other British Sources of Cardiff Building Stones.
*Igneous intrusive, granites*: 1, Aberdeen. 2, Craigton. 3, Peterhead. 4, Shap. 5, Bessbrook. 6, Penryn. 7, Carnsew. 8, Hantergantink. 9, De Lank; *dolerite*: 10, Pemnaenmawr. *Sedimentary*: 11, Corsehill. 12, St. Bees. 13, Darley Dale. 14, Derbyshire gritstone. 15, York Stone. 16, Hopton Wood. 17, Ashford Black ('marble'). 18, Grinshill. 19, N. Staffs. 20, Hornton. 21, Clipsham. 22, Chipping Camden. 23, Guiting. 24, Bath. 25, Box. 26, Corsham. 27, Ham Hill. 28, Portland. 29, Purbeck. 30, East Devon flint cobbles. 31, Beer. 32, Dundry. 33, Chellaston gypsum. 34, Doulting; '*marbles*' (*highly polishable limestones*): 35, Plymouth (Cardiff Castle). 36, Ipplepen (Cardiff Castle). 37, Kitley. 38, Ashburton. 39, Purbeck. *Metamorphic, slates*: 40, Blaenau Ffestiniog. 41, Nantlle Valley. 42, Burlington. 43, Coniston. 44, Lakeland Green. 45, Prescelly. 46, Delabole; *other metamorphic*: 47, Lizard serpentinite. 48, Iona marble (Roath parish church).

FIG. 4   European Sources of Cardiff Building Stones.
*Sedimentary*: 1, Irish red 'marble'. 2, Irish black 'marble'. 3, Caen Stone, France. 4,
Meureil 'marble', France. 5, Larrys 'marble', France. 6, Echaillon 'marble', France.
7, Napoleon 'marble', France. 8, Bleu Belge 'marble', Belgium. 9, Brocatelle 'marble', Spain (Cardiff Castle). 10, Red Aptian 'marble', Spain. 11, Santa Anna 'marble', Porugal (probably the source of the interior of the National Museum). 12,
Botticino 'marble', Italy. 13, Trani Mirabelle 'marble', Italy. *Igneous extrusive*: 14,
Naples lava. 15, Roman travertine. 16, Sicilian travertine. 17, Czechoslovakian
travertine. 18, Cannstadt travertine, Germany. *Igneous intrusive*: 19, Finnish Red
granite. 20, Baltic Brown granite, Finland. 21, Larvikite, Tjolling, Norway. 22, 23,
Imperial granite, Norway. 24, Black granite, Sweden. 25, Red granite, Sweden. 26,
Guernsey granite. 27, Sardinian granite. *Metamorphic*: 28, Alta skifer, Norway. 29,
Opdal skifer, Norway. 30, Barge quartzite, Italy. *Metamorphic, true marbles*: 31,
Portoro, Italy. 32, Rosso Levante, Italy. 33, Polcevera, Italy. 34, Verde Alpi, Italy.
35, Serevezza, Italy. 36, Carrara, Italy. 37, Paonazzo, Italy. 38, Siena, Italy. 39,
Tinos, Greece. 40, Verde Antico, Greece. 41, Pentelic, Greece.

and, while this increases the range of world geology we can examine, the problem of sources becomes more complex than ever.

The trails described demonstrate the wide variety of rocks used, beginning with one which is predominantly in local sedimentary rocks. The other trails bring in a wide range of British and foreign igneous and metamorphic rocks used in decorative finishes to shops and important public buildings.

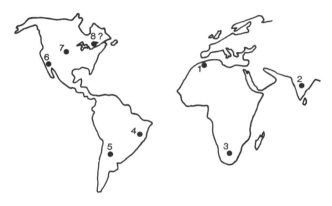

FIG. 5    Cardiff Building Stones from continents other than Europe.
1, Black granite, Morocco. 2, Black granite, India. 3, Black granite, South Africa. 4, Black granite, Brazil. 5, Verde Ermatita granite, N.W. Argentina. 6, Fire marble, California, U.S.A. (Cardiff Castle). 7, Imperial Mahogany granite, South Dakota, U.S.A. 8, High grade metamorphic setts, possible source in the St. Lawrence region.

# TRAIL 1:

## WYEVERNE ROAD – CORBETT ROAD – PARK PLACE – ST. ANDREW'S CRESCENT – WINDSOR PLACE

The terraced houses of Wyeverne Road reveal two of the principal local building stones, the upper Carboniferous Pennant Sandstones, grey when fresh, greenish brown here now that they have weathered, e.g. numbers 131–133, and pink-stained slightly hematised lower Carboniferous Limestone, numbers 143–145. There is little uniformity about this street. The houses were obviously built in pairs or small groups and walls with dressed and coursed stones are mingled with those of random work. Rounded blocks, obviously flood-plain cobbles dug from the foundations or close at hand, were also used. These cobbles are a feature of many Cardiff walls. They are generally of Pennant-type sandstones, sometimes of limestone, and less commonly of Devonian Old Red Sandstone, all clearly brought down by the River Taff.

The most interesting houses in Wyeverne Road are Nos. 139–141. They are partly built of ballast stones, vesicular lava blocks, probably from the Naples area. These houses also exhibit white Carboniferous Limestone blocks and Carboniferous sandstones, while their upper floors have much roughly squared granite.

Walk NW to the junction with Woodville Road. The capping to the boundary wall of the modern student hall of residence is of Radyr Stone, perhaps the most unusual of the local stones. This is a Permo-Triassic breccia, accumulated as a desert debris or alluvial fan at the foot of the slopes north of Cardiff 275 million years ago, from the erosion of the coalfield rim during the existence of the ancient supercontinent known as Pangaea, when South Wales lay in the latitudes of the present day Sahara. The irregular white clasts are mainly of Carboniferous Limestone, and the presence of much lime in solution accounts for the subsequent cementing and hardness of this originally loose desert sand and debris.

Radyr Stone is tough enough for engineering purposes, e.g.

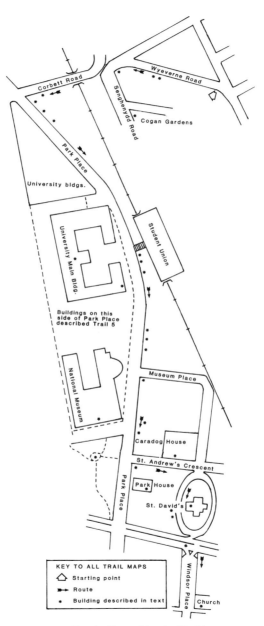

FIG. 6    Route Map for Trail 1.

FIG. 7 Vesicular lava ballast stone in the wall of No. 139 Wyeverne Road, probably derived from the Naples region.

Three Arches railway viaduct, the older of the two arches in Fidlas Road and Llanishen station are all built with it. Such a stone, composed of rough embedded lumps, would be termed a 'puddingstone' by builders.

Radyr Stone was quarried close to the west bank of the Taff, north-west of Llandaff Bridge. The deposit was eventually exhausted, but it lasted from about 1850 to the 1920s and, generally, this dates any building which incorporates the stone. Dating can only be approximate, however, for similar deposits at Cadoxton near Barry were also worked for buildings in Cardiff. Turn into Senghenydd Road for a short diversion down to the triangular garden in Cogan Place. Here large slabs of Radyr Stone have been set on edge as boundary walling and the stumps of iron railings which were formerly embedded in them have cleaved the blocks down their bedding planes in similar fashion to the quarrymen's wedges.

Return and cross the railway bridge into Corbett Road. Beyond the rear lane of Park Place, the side boundary wall of No. 69 is of richly fossiliferous Blue Lias limestone from the

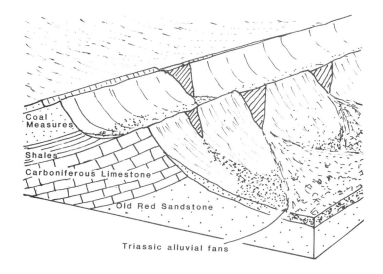

FIG. 8    Formation of the Radyr Stone as a Triassic desert alluvial fan.

FIG. 9    Bivalves (mainly oysters) in section, in Blue Lias Limestone blocks, wall to side of No. 69 Park Place.

Vale of Glamorgan coastal quarries and cliffs. The shells seen in section are mainly oysters, plus occasional larger bivalves such as *Plagiostoma*. About half way along the wall, its lower part is an older structure, of Carboniferous Limestone with the outlines of large *Productus* brachiopods visible.

Enter Park Place. The former houses at the upper end of Park Place are generally of machine-pressed brick with Bath Stone window dressings and quoins. Bath Stone is a broad term for the golden-coloured oolitic limestones from the Great Oolite of the Jurassic. There are many varieties and qualities, which were quarried from numerous mines and pits worked in the districts between Bath, Bradford-on-Avon and Corsham in Wiltshire. Therefore positive identification of the source often depends on written records than on visual examination. Bath Stone is one of Cardiff's more important building stones – indeed it was so in nearly every town in the land from the mid-nineteenth century to the inter-war years. Its use spread over the whole kingdom with the coming of the railways. Used as a foil to contrast with local stones, and later wth brick, it was as cheap as the latter. In 1856 it costs 1s.0d. – 1s.2d (5–6p) per cubic foot in Cardiff. However, as will be seen below, it came to the city in small amounts long before the railway era.

Bath Stone enjoyed its popularity because it is easily worked and carved when green, i.e. still with its quarry sap or ground-water. It hardens on exposure and then has a life in the building of at least 100 years. However, if the cement pointing around it is not kept in good order, frost will attack it and flaking off follows. Therefore much of Cardiff's nineteenth century stone-work is now at a critical age.

The garden boundary walls at the top of Park Place are capped with fine-grained Carboniferous sandstone. The best for carving came from the Forest of Dean quarries near Bix-head. These slabs are the variety known as Forest of Dean Grey.

The porches of Nos. 63–68 have columns of pink Triassic sandstone which are weathering rather badly because they are false-bedded. It is an invariable rule that sedimentary building stones must be laid 'on the bed', i.e. the same way up in the building as in the natural bedding of the deposit, so that the natural bedding planes are protected within the horizontal junctions of the wall.

## NATURAL BEDDING

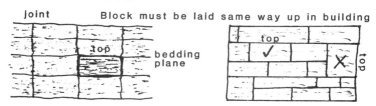

## COLUMNS from sedimentary rocks

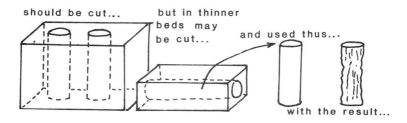

## COPING STONES

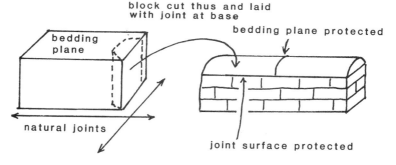

FIG. 10    Methods of laying building stones of sedimentary type.

The Triassic sandstones in these columns are arkose, i.e. of felspar grains, and were quarried in the N.W. Midlands, mainly in Staffordshire. However, the beds are not deep enough to cut vertical columns from. They could only be cut along the bed and then 'stood up' in the building. Hence the weathering and flaking as natural bedding lineations, running up the columns, have been attacked.

Beyond the staircase to the University Union building, a visual disaster built of brown-dyed calc-silicate bricks of unrivalled drabness, study the stone wall bounding the grounds of a University Chaplaincy. It reveals the deltaic and flood-plain river deposits of the Carboniferous Coal Measure sandstones, remnants of the lush tropical rain forest and the precipitation of ironstones which occurred 300 million years ago as South Wales drifted northwards across the Equator. Starting at the first pavement slab below the straight length of the wall, count the pavement slabs to identify your position in the description which follows:

The wall is random built for the first 44 paving slabs length and many blocks are face-bedded, i.e. their bedding planes are wrongly laid to form the face of the wall:

Above slabs 3–4: several blocks reveal bedding planes covered with carbonised plant debris and glistening coal fragments.

Above slabs 12–14: a block low down near the pavement exposes plant stem fragments, preserved in sideritic ironstone.

Above slab 20: a block 0.9m above the footpath shows a section through a deposit of sideritic ironstone nodules. The deposit was formed by the winnowing out of an originally mixed deposit of nodules and sandstone. It was reworked by a migrating river channel in the deltaic and swampy conditions of the upper Carboniferous. This removed much of the original sand, leaving the ironstone nodules behind, concentrated into a lag deposit. Nodules such as these, about 30 per cent iron ore, were the first basis of the South Wales iron industry.

Above slab 24: 46cm up, another seam of ironstone nodules crossing the middle of a block, and more nodules in a block 1.8m up.

Above slab 26: a whole block of ironstone nodules 1.2m up and to its right a sandstone with carbonised plant fragments.

Above slab 40: more nodules in a block 1.2.m up.

Above slab 43: more plant and coal fragment bearing blocks.

Slab 44 and the end of the random walling: 1.5m up a ripple-marked bedding surface with carbonised material preserved in the ripple troughs.

No. 46 provides the first example seen on these trails of another way of using stone – joint bedding it as wall coping. Here, very shelly Bath Stone, with the shell fragments weathering proud of the surfaces, reveals cross-bedding. The rocks have clearly been laid on their side, so that the joint is hidden

FIG. 11    Sideritic Ironstone nodules from the Coal Measure sandstones; wall of University Catholic Chaplaincy, Park Place.

in the base of the slabs and the bedding plane protected between neighbouring sections of the coping.

No. 40 has a bay window whose columns reveal bands of siliceous mineral weathering proud of the surrounding limestone; also porch columns of pink Scottish granite, see below. Nos. 39–40 have landscaped frontages of embedded flint beach cobbles, revealing chatter-marked surfaces. Widely used now as a means of discouraging pedestrians on central reservations of roads, etc., these are extracted from the beaches of Axmouth and Seaton on the East Devon coast and are of Cretaceous age.

The front doorsteps of No. 43 and especially the left hand steps to the Midland Bank, No. 36, are constructed of Lower Cambrian slates, probably from the Nantle Valley area of Snowdonia. Their purple colour is interrupted by en echelon patches of green iron reduction spots. The spots form by migration of iron soon after the deposition of the sediment and were originally spherical. Folding and cleavage of the rocks during the Caledonian orogeny caused elongation of the spots in the direction of the cleavage.

Cross Museum Place to Nos. 33–34, a pair of houses with an interesting polychrome effect, the builder seeking to lighten

FIG. 12   Iron reduction spots showing elongation in direction of cleavage, in purple Lower Cambrian slates from Snowdonia. Midland Bank steps, Park Place.

the sombre appearance of the Pennant Sandstone with a mixture of pink-stained Carboniferous Limestone, reddish sandstones (probably arkose Triassic sandstones from Staffordshire), and an occasional block of Radyr Stone. Crinoids, cross-bedding and sandstone-conglomerate junctions within a single block are among the features to observe. The porch of No. 34 has columns of fine-grained pink Scottish granite, from quarries near Peterhead, possibly Stirlinghill Quarry. Proceed to No. 28, the British Council Offices, where the base of the garden wall is of coursed Blue Lias limestone. This is an easy rock to lay in courses, because of the consistent depth of its individual beds.

No. 26, National Westminster Bank. A slab-clad building. Sawing stone into slabs (usually about 2.5cm thick) became fashionable as a means of decorating buildings from the 1920s onwards. The fashion began in France and Belgium and was frowned on by many as a use of stone 'without any architectural or human interest'. This treatment is usually carried out in igneous or metamorphic rocks capable of taking a high decorative polish.

The facade of this bank may have a beauty which is only 'skin deep' but it is an interesting one. The plinth and the steps are in Lakeland Green Slates. These slates are not true slates but compacted volcanic ashes from the Middle Tuffs of the Ordovician Borrowdale Volcanic Series. Banding and colour variation can be seen in them, for these originally air-fall materials were water-laid and thus show graded bedding and channel structures. These green slates are quarried at Coniston and in Langdale in the Lake District. The wall claddings are in white Carrara marble from Italy, while below the windows there are panels of 'black granite', actually a gabbro or diorite.

Geologically there is no such thing as a black granite, for granites are acid rocks, rich in quartz and therefore light in colour. Black Granite is a stone trade name for this rock which is also known as Ebony Black. It is a favourite below shop-front windows and has many sources, all the old shield areas of the world, e.g. the Baltic, Africa or India. In each case the rock may have originally been a granite or gabbro, but it has suffered great alteration. Formerly white-coloured minerals such as felspar and quartz have become filled with iron ore and ferro-magnesian minerals, making the rock an overall dense black.

Buildings of pre-1940 age generally obtained their black granite from Finland or Sweden. More recently the market has been supplied from Morocco, South Africa, India or Brazil, e.g. the Bonaccord Black variety. Looked at closely, these black granites are mainly plagioclase felspar and augite. Close examination of the surface with a hand lens may reveal polished steely-looking iron ore. This is magnetite.

Cross St. Andrew's Place to No. 22 where the gate pillars are of Pennant Sandstone, and the boundary wall of pink-stained Carboniferous Limestone. This stone has been widely used in many city walls, particularly where road re-alignments have taken place. It is unfortunately known as 'Radyr Pink' and must not be confused by name with the Triassic Radyr Stone, already seen.

FIG. 13    Park House, Park Place. Pennant Sandstones with Bath Stone dressings and pink granite porch columns. The roof is of two different coloured slates from North Wales.

No. 20, Park House, built in 1874 by William Burges for the Marquis of Bute's agent, is a famous Cardiff house. It is of Pennant Sandstone with Bath Stone dressings. Columns of evenly-grained pink Scottish granite from Caledonian age intrusions at Craigton quarry in Aberdeen and quarries further north at Peterhead adorn the porch and verandah. The finer-grained seen here is from Craigton, with quartz no more prominent than the other minerals. The Peterhead ones are coarser in grain size, with more quartz, but both types derive their pink colour from their orthoclase felspars. The columns were produced in standard lengths and diameters usually, not to individual builder's or architect's orders, and appear in many Cardiff houses.

Return to St. Andrew's Place and walk east. On the north side of the street stands Caradog House, again a calc-silicate brick building. These bricks are fired from mixes of brick clays and silica. Known as sand-limes or flint-limes according to the aggregate used, their colour comes from adding permanent inactive dyes, not from their position within the kiln as with clay bricks. Calc-silicates are fired in steam autoclaves for 6–10 hours. They give consistent shape, texture and colour and, unlike clay bricks, have no soluble sulphides to cause subsequent salt efflorescence and flaking problems. Any unfused lime in them sets on exposure, thus increasing their hardness. How different this building is from the University Union building! Caradog House has warmth, a range of tones and the added textural effect of recessed pointing.

Enter Windsor Place. Eglwys Dewi Sant (1863) shows many local stones in its walls and also something of Cardiff's building traditions. Examine the west frontage. Pennant Sandstones form the base of the walls, with some Carboniferous Limestone, up to the first course of Bath Stone. The walls above have dressings and quoins of Bath Stone, followed inwards by dressed and coursed Pennant and then by random polygonal jointing which is a Kentish Ragstone style, possibly brought to Cardiff by migrant building workers. The latter reveals light grey Carboniferous Limestone, red Old Red Sandstone and Radyr Stone breccia, and Carboniferous Millstone Grit quartz conglomerates, some being former river cobbles. The western porch roof is of shelly, cross-bedded Bath Stone. Extensions either side of the west front follow the same style but are dominated by Pennant Sandstone, some with carbonised plant fragments, and Carboniferous Limestone, some with brachiopods visible.

Some former houses nearby reveal further examples of slate steps with iron reduction spots, while the pavements around the church are of Pennine gritstone slabs. From Derbyshire or West Yorkshire, many of these Coal Measure (Elland Flags) or Millstone Grit aged rocks (Rough Rock Flags) show parting lineation. This type of paving was widely used in nineteenth century towns. The most important quarries were around Brighouse, Halifax and Leeds, e.g. Farnley and Morley. All sources come under the general name of York Stone. Some paving of this type was also imported from Ireland.

Cross the dual carriageway, noting the flint beach cobbles of the central reservation, and walk down the east side to the United Reformed Church, 1866. It is notable for the use of Radyr Stone at the top of all its decorative arch details, but is otherwise the usual Pennant Sandstone with Bath Stone dressings.

## TRAIL 2:

## NEWPORT ROAD – QUEEN STREET AND ADJACENT PARTS OF CHURCHILL WAY, WINDSOR AND PARK PLACES, AND CHARLES STREET

This trail starts at the western entrance to the Cardiff Royal Infirmary:

*Newport Road, south side*

The western frontage of the Infirmary, adjacent to Newport Road, is occupied by the chapel wall, a fine example of random polygonal jointing using local Carboniferous Limestone with Bath Stone dressings. The rest of the frontage mainly employs Pennant and Old Red Sandstones. Cross Glossop Road.

St. James's Church: This is built of pale pink well-laminated and crinoidal limestone, of Carboniferous age. Known as Swelldon Stone, it was quarried in the Saintwell inlier S.E. of Culverhouse Cross and belongs to the Z zone (Chadian/Courceyan). The dressings of St. James's are in the best of the Bath Stones, the very resistant Box Ground Stone from Hazelbury near Box, and the boundary wall is of Pennant with Radyr Stone coping.

The South Glamorgan County Headquarters has panels of Lakeland Green Slate below the windows. Below the porch the wall cladding is of dark Larvikite (Emerald Pearl variety) from Norway. This is quarried at Tjolling near Larvik on the west side of Oslo Fjord. It is one of the many intrusive rocks of Permian age which occur in the Oslo Graben and is an alkali syenite. Its remarkable attraction comes from the schillerisation – the reflection of light from planes within its large blue crystals of labradorite felspar. Turn your head as you examine it and the felspars show polarisation, alternatively reflecting and going into extinction as the view point is changed. Oligoclase and alkali felspar are present in these crystals, the plagioclase felspars showing intricate twinning. In this dark variety of larvikite the groundmass is not easily visible, but it contains clots of titan-augite, iron-rich olivine, plenty of apatite and irregular masses of iron ore, some being titano-magnetite.

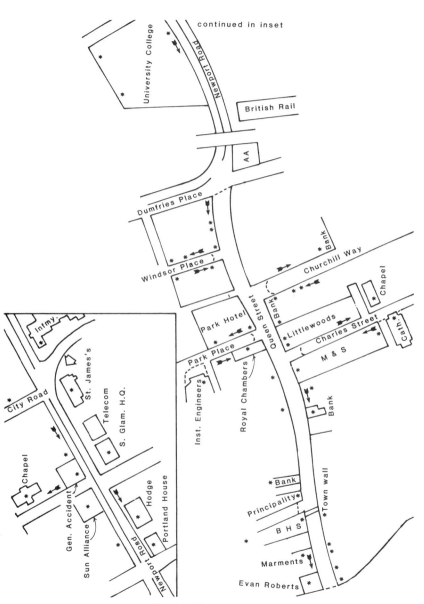

FIG. 14    Route Map for Trail 2.

At the Julian Hodge Building note the steps and entrance pathway, paved in a micaceous metamorphic stone, probably of Norwegian origin. Many quarries in Norway produce similar metamorphosed slatey rocks. They are known as skifer. This may be the Opdal or Alta variety, a quartz slate (kvartskifer).

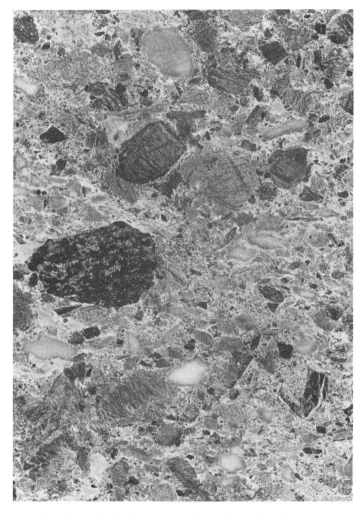

FIG. 15   The Greek Marble Verde Antico from Thessaly, with brecciated green serpentinite blocks. Portland House, Newport Road.

Portland House building has a ground-floor cladding of the Greek Verde Antico marble. Quarried at Casambala N.E. of Larissa in Thessaly, this is the light variety. A notable feature is the white mineral which has intruded the vein material, its patches blurring into the surrounding green areas.

## Newport Road, north side

Before walking west from the junction with City Road, go up that road a short distance to the first shop on the right which has panels of red granite. The blood-red felspars are closely packed and amount to about half the volume of the rock which is probably the variety named Rosso Rubino in Italy, but could originate in the United States where its name is Colorado Red. Such are the perils of comparing stone trade names with true geological names and origins! Return to Newport Road and walk west.

The Allied Irish Bank has dark grey Cornish granite steps and a porch lined with Lakeland Green Slate.

General Accident Offices: Porch lined with creamy-brown marble with brown veins, possibly Calacatta Grotte or the Cipollino Dorato from Valdieri or Framosa in the Piemonte region of the Italian Alps. The steps are of light grey Bodmin Moor granite.

FIG. 16    Corals and stylolites in dark grey Carboniferous Limestone, wall of Tredegarville Baptist Chapel, off Newport Road. The stone is probably from Ireland.

Walk to the rear of the General Accident Offices and examine the Tredegarville Chapel, a somewhat startling building of contrasting white and dark grey limestones. From their fossil content, both appear to be of Carboniferous Age. On some of the dark-grey bituminous blocks, black stylolites can be seen, the graph-like lines formed by pressure solution, and there are crinoids, brachiopods, worm burrows and corals. The latter include some fine examples (of *Syringopora* ?) on the outer side of the wall. There is an interesting tradition about this chapel. It was built by the Cory family, allegedly from ballast stones brought back in their coal boats from Italy. However, it is much more likely that the boats called at Galway on the return journey and obtained the stone from there.

Fig. 17    Entrance to the Sun Alliance offices, Newport Road, panelled with brecciated serpentinite marble from Tinos and surrounded by frames of travertine, black 'granite' and Portland Stone.

Sun Alliance Offices: ground floor, a 'black granite' plinth with Portland Stone cladding above. Notice the shell debris in the Portland Stone – this must be present in natural slabs and is the key to distinguish true Portland Stone blocks from concrete imitations of it. (The same applies to the golden coloured

Bath Stones where there should also be shelly debris and certainly a visible oolitic texture.) The porch is lined with panels of Greek marble, an irregularly brecciated serpentinite from the island of Tinos in the Aegean Sea. The marble is surrounded by golden travertine from the Rome region and a frame of 'black granite'. Travertine is the cavity riddled calcium carbonate deposit associated with steam and hot spring activity in old volcanic districts. The creamy-coloured type comes from numerous quarries around the Rome region of Italy, e.g. the Tivoli quarries, or from Sicily. There is also a deep golden variety which may be Italian, but other sources of that are found at Cannstadt, near Stuttgart, Germany, and in Czechoslovakia. In some examples the natural cavities are subsequently stopped in by further migrations of mineral material, but if not this can be done with resins, sometimes of similar colour but on other examples in contrasting black. Above the ground floor all the windows have surrounds of Italian white Carrara marble with panels below them of slabbed Portland Roach, Upper Jurassic. Roach, a general quarryman's term for rough material, is the cavernous bedding which occurs in the top of the Portland Stone beds in Dorset. It was formerly used only for engineering purposes, e.g. breakwaters, etc., but lately in a fashion started by U.S.A. stone merchants it has been sawn for decorative claddings. The cavernous appearance is due to the solution and removal of fossil shells, etc., which were originally buried in its limy sediment, chiefly the lamellibranch *Laevitrigonia*, the turreted gastropod *Aptyxiella portlandica* and the lime-grain trapping calcareous red alga *Solenopora*.

West of the Sun Alliance Office the boundary wall is of Carboniferous Limestone, the local 'Radyr Pink', and the porch of the Oddfellows Hall has panels of Italian brecciated serpentinite marbles.

Cross West Grove to the frontage of University College Cardiff's Newport Road site. To the east end of the 1918 frontage, steps to an old doorway show iron reduction spots on blue Cambrian slates. The cappings of the boundary wall to the west show shelly debris in Portland Stone with some fine algal structures, especially the left hand pillar beyond the main entrance, about 1.4m above pavement level – the red alga *Solenopora*. The frontage of the building is of Bath Stone and brick and the main entrance has fine Derbyshire gritstone steps

(Millstone Grit, Carboniferous). The Bath Stone facings on the building at the rear, facing the Parade, are of Corsham Down Bath Stone (Metallurgy and Materials Science Department, the former Medical School). The more recent building to the west, the Mineral Exploitation department, also has panels of Jurassic oolitic limestone, some of which are very fossiliferous.

*Queen Street*

Roopa Jean Centre, No. 137, has a window frame of dark green, brecciated serpentinite marble, probably the Italian Verde Alpi from the Val d'Aosta in the Italian Alps. It may be appropriate here to write about serpentinites for there are many examples in shop fronts. They are mainly dark green rocks, though some have added red coloration. They are composed largely of the mineral serpentine, strongly veined and, hence, giving a good figuration when polished. Many were originally lavas or intrusive rocks poor in quartz; all have subsequently been metamorphosed. Some were metamorphosed in mid-ocean submarine ridge settings and are remnants of ophiolites, others in tectonic situations involving mountain building, e.g. the Alpine movements. In many of the latter extensive brecciation has then taken place. The many green varieties of serpentinite come from the Piemonte region of Italy, especially the Val d'Aosta, or northern Greece (Larissa and Thessalonika) while red serpentinites are supplied from Liguria in Italy or The Lizard area of Cornwall.

Yorkshire Building Society, No. 125; finely brecciated green marble from the island of Tinos, Greece. DER Television Rental, No. 125; window frame of grey slate. Cross to the south side of the street, where the Halifax Building Society No. 124, has panels of the light Blue Pearl larvikite over a plinth of 'black granite'. Walk west to No. 120, David Edwards jewellers, where there is an example of the Formica imitation marble, soon discovered by a few finger taps! Cross to the north side again.

The frontage of Barclays Bank/Austin Reed's, No. 121, has a plinth of 'black granite' below the windows. The steps are in two types of Cornish granite, the lighter-coloured one having small felspar phenocrysts. The main facade of the building above is ashlar-faced in Portland Stone. Note the calcite outlines of shelly debris on the surfaces. The shop front to Austin

Reed is of stopped Roman travertine, using a light-coloured resin, the best examples being the panels on the entrance doors in Windsor Place. Continue into Windsor Place, east side.

FIG. 18  The Royal Insurance Building in Windsor Place, a granite and larvikite clad building with some marble and quartzite.

Royal Insurance Building, No. 39 Windsor Place. A fine example of the steel-frame slab-clad modern building, quite richly covered. The ground floor has a 'black granite' plinth with panels of Cornish (Hercynian) granite showing nests of biotite. These panels are continued on the higher floors where the outer frame of the building is faced with Portland Limestone (Upper Jurassic), whereas the frame to the ground floor is of light blue larvikite. This is Blue Pearl larvikite or, in Italian stone trade literature, *claro* whereas the dark one is called the Emerald Pearl or *scuro*. The light blue variety has a greater density of schillerising felspars. The porch of the building is also framed in larvikite, with the entrance framed in 'black granite', with panels of white Italian Carrara marble. The steps are edged with Cornish granite but the risers and the paving are of Barge Quartzite, a metamorphic rock from Barge near Monte Bracco in the Italian Alps. More Carrara marble can be seen lining the entrance porch to Caerwys House (Legal & General Office) a few yards to the north. With the exception of the Pentelic marble from Greece, all white marbles come from the Carrara district and are true marbles, being metamorphosed from limestones of Lower Jurassic (Lias) age as proved by fossils found there. The marble may be plain white or variously veined in grey or golden colours, sometimes also with nests of other minerals. The stone trade has a variety of names for the Carrara marbles, some of which are geographically misleading, e.g. all grey-veined types are called Sicilian, while all greyish types are termed Bardiglian. The Pentelic marble from Greece can be distinguished from the Italian whites by its wispy brownish streaks which are due to iron pyrites, cubes of which can sometimes be seen with a hand lens.

Cross to the west side of Windsor Place. Lloyds Bank is faced on the ground floor with a green mottled and veined metamorphic rock of unknown provenance which may be another variety of Norwegian stone. Walk back towards Queen Street. Summit House has risers to its steps in a grey variety of Italian *conglomerato*. These are slabbed materials made from true marble, limestone or travertine fragments embedded in resins of suitable colour, the whole process being done in large tanks. From the resulting blocks the usual frame-sawing produces these slabs. They do look remarkably like true brecciated marbles, with fine chips scattered in the apparent veins. However, you can always tell the difference from the polish. The resin veins do not take it as well as the rock fragments. The latter feel slightly proud of the 'veins'. Nearly all the Italian marbles are now produced in true and *conglomerato* versions.

Cooke & Arkwright, No. 7; panelled between and below the windows with a white-veined green brecciated serpentinite marble, Italian. Leicester Building Society, No. 5; grey Cornish granite panels at pavement level and behind the name sign; ground floor clad with 'black granite'. Benedictos; the Greek marble Verde Antico, the same one seen at Portland House in Newport Road, but of larger size pieces. Re-enter Queen Street and cross south to Churchill Way.

Churchill Way, east side; starting at the Savoy Restaurant which has panels of white Carrara marble over a 'black granite' plinth, walk to the Guardian Royal Exchange Building. The Midland Bank on the ground floor of this building has an open porch on the south-west corner, clad in panels of grey and white marble, with a floor set with green serpentinite blocks. Along the rest of the ground floor frontages the shops are framed with Carrara marble with prominent grey veining, while below the bank windows, grey marble with white-filled tension gashes is the Noire Vein or Bleu Belge from the Ardennes. Cross to the west side of the street.

Churchill Way Post Office has panels of brecciated angular serpentinite marble in which some large boulders can be seen. This is the Polcevera marble from north of Genoa in Liguria, Italy. The National & Provincial Building Society is decorated with the Blue Pearl larvikite while the offices of James, Jones and Henton provide another example of a green brecciated marble, with white veins, some of which show en echelon tension gash structures. The National Westminster Bank at the corner of Queen Street has a ground floor built of the resistant variety of Bath Stone, the Box Ground Stone, and on its Queen Street frontage there are columns of Portland Stone. Cross to the Park Hotel opposite.

The Park Hotel building, 1885. Much of its interest was revealed during cleaning a few years ago. The ground floor is in Forest of Dean Blue, the Carboniferous Pennant-type sandstone from Bixslade. The stone frames the shop frontages on the Queen Street facade, but the most interesting area is along the Park Place frontage where the stone has weathered badly

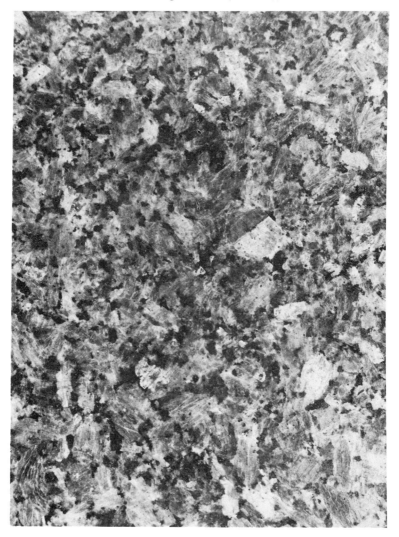

FIG. 19    Blue Pearl larvikite from Tjolling, Norway, with large, schillerising felspar crystals. National & Provincial Building Society offices, Churchill Way.

up to the window sill level. Before the pedestrianisation of Queen Street, Park Place was a much busier road and the weathering is probably due to winter salt spray being thrown against the building.

FIG. 20a   The Park Hotel; its ground floor faced with Forest of Dean Blue stone. The floors above with Pennant Sandstone, Bath Stone and terracotta dressings.

FIG. 20b    Hantergantink granite, a Hercynian age fine-grained granite with streaks of biotite, from Bodmin Moor, Cornwall. Britannia Building Society offices, S.W. corner of the Park Hotel.

Forest of Dean Stone was brought to Cardiff from 1836 onwards, in the pre-railway age by boat from Lydney. Notice the fine grain of the sandstone, with little evidence of bedding features. Its qualities in building work are obvious, e.g. the sharp angles and rebates which can be carved in it, and although the ground floor is badly weathered here, Forest of Dean Stone was generally valued in Cardiff for its resistance to impure atmospheres. The Blue variety occurs below the Grey, about 33–36m below the surface, in beds 0.8m thick. The Blue cost more than the Grey because of its superior colour and texture (see Royal Chambers opposite for the Grey variety). Other Dean quarries providing it were those at Fetterhill (Old Foggy) and Gorsty Knoll.

Two other items of note occur on the ground floor. Firstly the fine-grained Hantergantink granite from Bodmin Moor (St. Breward), cladding the office of the Britannia Building Society on the corner of the building and exhibiting nests and streaks of biotite, and secondly, the Perlato travertine *conglomerato* panelling to the Theatre Suite entrance, an ill-chosen match with the rest of the building.

The upper floors of the Park Hotel are faced in Pennant Sandstone with Bath Stone dressings. Recent cleaning has revealed much terracotta work as well. Made from fine-sieved clay pressed into gypsum firing moulds, terracotta is generally red or creamy-buff in colour and was popular with Victorian builders, no doubt following Prince Albert's championship of the form, the Royal Albert Hall, etc. Park Hotel has panels of it below each upper window, adorned with swags of fruit and flowers, and the little curving arches of it with small rosettes above the windows. The largest terracotta decorations however, are the serrated rows of modillions below the top cornice of the building and the consoles at the top of the pillars. High above the Theatre Suite entrance some of these have been damaged and their hollow interiors can be seen, thus proving that they are of terracotta and not of carved stonework. Cross to the west side of Park Place.

The South Wales Institute of Engineers building, 1897, shows how Victorian architects were adapting brick and terracotta to form intricately ornamented buildings that would have previously been carried out in carved stonework. It is built of machine-pressed bricks from St. Julian's in Newport, Old Red Sandstone deposits. Many of the mouldings are also in this brick, but there are panels of terracotta too and of carved red sandstones, probably Triassic from Corsehill near Annan in Dumfriesshire. Corsehill Stone is freely turned and carved, being a Triassic deposit of dark red to pale pink colour, with quartz and felspar grains cemented by silica and calcium and magnesium carbonates. The walls and gate-posts also have carved red sandstone cappings. Return towards Queen Street and stop at the entrance to Royal Chambers.

Royal Chambers. The porch is framed with a polished deep red Scandinavian granite with blue reflections from crush-planes within its quartz crystals. The building is faced with the Grey Forest of Dean Stone, fortunately recently cleaned so the full contrast with the Blue variety in the Park Hotel opposite can now be seen. Re-enter Queen Street and cross to Littlewoods Store.

Dunns/John Menzies, 90–92 Queen Street. Panels above are arranged in a tile effect, and of a blue metamorphic stone, probably another example of the Norwegian quartz skifer from Opdal or Alta.

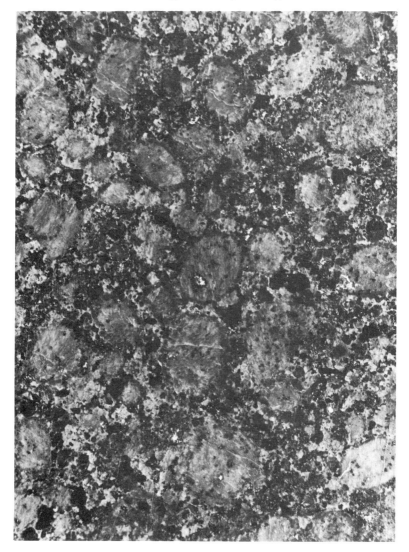

FIG. 21 Rapakivi texture with quartz haloes surrounding large felspar crystals, in Baltic Brown granite from Finland. Littlewoods Store.

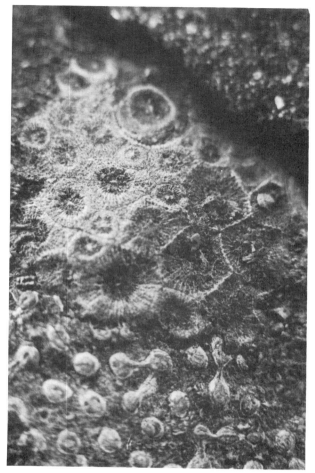

FIG. 22   Carboniferous Limestone with the coral *Lonsdaleia floriformis*, Ebeneser Chapel, Charles Street.

Littlewoods Store. The shop frontage here has been recently renewed in reddish-brown granite, the superb rapakivi-textured Baltic Granite from Finland. This is a Precambrian granite, quarried close to the Russian border, not far from the Gulf of Finland. It has distinctive large, round felspar crystals in which the flesh-coloured potash felspar core is mantled by a rim of small oligoclase grains. The large crystals are sur-

rounded by a groundmass of quartz, biotite and smaller felspars. The quartz is often clustered in haloes around the large
felspars, which may also have enclosed flakes of biotite and
reach a few centimetres in diameter. Continue down Charles
Street, noting the dark xenolith in the Baltic Granite panels of
the side entrance to Littlewoods.

Ebeneser Chapel (built 1955 originally as the Charles Street
Congregational Chapel, but taken over by the Ebeneser Chapel
following demolition of that building which stood on the site
of the Debenham Store in the St. David's Centre). This is an
amazing building – it could well be called the 'Ballast Chapel'
of Cardiff and is the only major building in Cardiff to make use
of these materials which were normally relegated to the friezes
and back lanes of housing districts. At the time of its construc-
tion the members were pleased to think that the building
incorporated a stone from every country in the world. Literally,
that is very unlikely, but the range is certainly enormous and
the idea no doubt came from the use of the ballast and the
knowledge of the wide range of Cardiff's coal trade. The dressings are of Bath Stone, with the western entrance steps of Portland Stone. The dressings of the plinth are of Carboniferous
sandstones, some of the blocks displaying large flakes of mus-
covite (white mica). The random polygonal walling includes
Old Red Sandstones; Pennant Sandstones; several varieties of
granites and dolerites; Millstone Grit quartz conglomerates;
Carboniferous Limestones including the pink Creigiau/Pen-
tyrch and the paler Swelldon varieties; and schists and blocks
of chert. The Carboniferous Limestones reveal superb
examples of corals, *Lithostrotion*, *Syringopora* and *Lonsdaleia
floriformis*, in the wall to the side entrance steps at the south-
west corner, the steps being of Derbyshire gritstone (Namurian
Millstone Grit, Carboniferous). Walk down to the end of
Charles Street. On the opposite side of the junction with Bridge
Street, Lloyds Bank is clad with panels of red serpentinite,
laced with veins of white quartz. Return up the west side of
Charles Street.

St. David's R.C. Cathedral, 1887. Walled with Pennant Sandstone, it is the dressings which are of interest. Of orange-red
Triassic sandstones, the blocks reveal cross-bedding and are
from arkose deposits, either from North Staffordshire or from
Grinshull near Shrewsbury. Just north of the cathedral a rear

corner pillar to the Marks & Spencer store is clad with the French Napoleon Marble from the Pas de Calais, see below. Re-enter Queen Street.

Marks & Spencer, No. 72 Queen Street, exhibits one of the most unusual stones seen anywhere in Cardiff. It is the Verde Ermatita, from the Andean cordillera at San Juan in N.W. Argentina and lines the frontage behind the name sign above the windows. It can be seen at street level in the panels around the doorway to the stairs on the right. Verde Ermatita is also referred to as Madreperla and sometimes as Ermatita Granite, but is identified as a dark-green contact-metamorphosed gneiss, with blue cordierite visible.

Cross to the north side of Queen Street where the frontage to W.H. Smith and Greenfield is of grey-veined Carrara marble with nests of a darker mineral. Further examples of Carrara marble occur on the south side of the street in the premises of Ernest Jones, No. 62 and Olympus Sports, No. 60. Notice the fine Bath Stone frontage of Andrews Buildings (1896) above the shop fronts opposite. Continue west to the Midland Bank.

Midland Bank, Nos 56–58, 1918. The base of this building is faced with evenly-grained grey Cornish granite, with squarish felspar crystals. Recent granite installations around an auto-bank dispenser and night safe have not been matched, however. Around these is a new coarser granite with more numerous and buff-coloured felspars. This is probably the Sardinian Beige granite which has become very fashionable in recent years. It has a very even crystal texture with grey and buff felspars and quartz crystals of much the same size. Currently it is the lowest-priced granite and large quantities of it are now being imported.

Cross the street to the H.M.V. Record Shop, No. 51, where the window frame provides further examples of the rapakivi-textured Baltic Granite from Finland. Installed in 1979, this was the first example of this granite in Cardiff. Returning to the south side, the frontage of Boots (Chemists) above street level is clad with ashlared blocks of Portland Stone. Opposite Boots is another of the gems of Queen Street.

Lloyds Bank, 31 Queen Street. The richness of the stonework on this building is incredible. The ground floor is faced with blue larvikite and red granite while the rest of the facade above is of carved Portland Stone. The red granite contains blue

FIG. 23   Lloyds Bank, No. 31 Queen Street, with ground floor of red granite and larvikite, Portland Stone above.

quartz and is the Precambrian Virgo Granite from Sweden. It has suffered slight crushing, causing the development of reflective planes within its quartz crystals. The steps to the office entrances on the left are of grey and white Italian marble, possibly the Greggio Carnico variety.

The Principality Building Society, 1914, on the corner of Queen Street and the Friary, is built of the Ridge Park Stone, a variety of Bath Stone. 'Black granite' panels are set below the windows facing Queen Street, while the corner doorway has plinths of grey Cornish granite on either side. The Friary frontage windows are surrounded by panels of light grey and white veined marble, while the panels of the name above are in white Carrara, with grey veins, possibly the variety Dove Capella.

Cross to the west side of the Friary where Portland Stone ashlar and granite plinths are the rule, on both the Prudential Building and the side of British Home Stores. The former is beautifully polished and very fine-grained granite, the non-porphyritic Quarry or Blue granite of the South-west of England intrusions. It has much shadowy figuration, probably of imperfectly absorbed covering rocks. Examine the sidewall of British Home Stores for the shelly debris in the Portland Stone. Return to the corner of the shop facing Queen Street.

Notice the small square blocks of dolerite, laid in squares with brick surrounds which cross Queen Street's pavement. These may come from the Midland Valley of Scotland and they mark the line of the former town wall and East Gate of Cardiff. On the south side the end wall to the Dolcis shoe store, facing the frontage of Allders, is of blue Lower Cambrian slate from North Wales. Walk west to Timpsons, No. 16 where there are panels of green-brown brecciated serpentinite and then on to Pastiche, No. 12, which has another polished frontage of larvikite and red granite. Return to the north side at Marments Store.

Marments store, Nos. 11–17, was built in 1922 and has a fine Portland Stone frontage. The sections of the splendid columns reveal how such height can only be achieved by using many blocks. The depth obtainable from the best beds in the Portland Quarries would never suffice for such tall columns. Continue to the west end of Queen Street.

The former Evan Roberts store (Kingsway House) is a steel-framed slab-clad building with panels of dark larvikite below the windows and claddings of light Blue larvikite on the panels, portico and the rest of the facade above. White, grey-veined marble lines the course below the portico. On the south side of the street opposite, Evans Outsize, No. 4, has panels around the windows which are of a cream coloured marble, notable for the wavy graph-like lines which are due to pressure solution and are known as stylolites. This may be Botticino marble from near Brescia in Lombardy, Italy. Finally, the last premises on this trail, Palmer's jewellery shop, has panels of a *conglomerato*. Set in a darker resin that usual, the fragments resemble those of Breccia Aurora, also from near Brescia. The blocks are of shelly limestones with bryozoa, travertines, etc., and are mainly brown and black in colour.

# TRAIL 3:

# ST. JOHN'S SQUARE – TRINITY STREET – THE HAYES

Start on the east side of St. John's Square at the frontage of Palmer's jewellery shop. The side entrance porch of Refuge Assurance House, actually No. 2 Queen Street, is framed in dark grey granite with small squarish felspars. This is the Caledonian (Old Red Sandstone) aged granite from Bessbrook in Northern Ireland.

A series of building society offices follows, Anglian with creamy-coloured Italian Perlato *conglomerato* slabs, Halifax with 'black granite', Provincial with Devonian grey slates from Delabole in Cornwall, and Glamorgan with very highly polished 'black granite'. Walk south down Working Street to the western entrance to the St. David's Centre. Note the panels around the Allders windows, described with the account of the centre.

The St. David's Centre. This shopping precinct has some major features of geological interest. It has brought into the city extensive new examples of the Napoleon Tigre marble from the Carboniferous beds at Hydrequent in the Pas de Calais of N.E. France. The only previous use of this stone in Cardiff was in the western window pillars of Allders Store. The richly-mottled brown and white stone now forms the pillars between all the shops in the precinct, and is particularly well seen at the south end of Cathedral Walk, just outside the doors of the centre, on the sidewall to Marks & Spencer where there are pictures of Old Cardiff. The rock is a non-metamorphosed limestone. Many of its cloudy patches are of algal origin, but it is mainly a lime-mud deposit from shallow-water lagoons which were subject to periodic emergence. Recrystallisation of the muds then took place, with undulose layers filling in some of the cavities while clear calcite invaded others. Waves pounded, broke up and re-grouped the sediments.

The central features of the St. David's Centre, the fountains, plant beds, etc., are built up with a travertine *conglomerato* which is the one known as Perlato or Perlato Apia. Two other

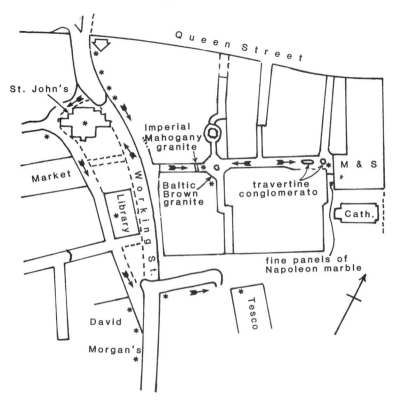

FIG. 24 Route Map for Trail 3.

features of interest lie near the main intersection. H. Samuel's shop has the rapakivi-textured Finnish Baltic Brown granite over its windows and, walking west towards Working Street, the line of the old town wall is marked by a band of deep red-brown granite paving. This is a really exciting addition to the stones of Cardiff. It is the American granite Imperial Mahogany, of Precambrian age from the basement rocks of the state of South Dakota. The rock has suffered deformation due to later mountain building periods and shows partly metamorphic textures, e.g. streaking out of felspars and mica into bands. The felspars show augen-like (lens or eye-like) bunching and internal crushing. Some slabs also show prominent veins. In some examples of this rock, the veins can be up to 8cm

Fig. 25 Napoleon Tigre marble, Carboniferous, from Hydrequent, Pas de Calais, France. Used in the St. David's Centre and in the frontage of Pizzaland in High Street.

wide, lined with pink crystals and filled with coarse growths of quartz. The rock should really be called a gneiss because of its metamorphic features. The plaques commemorating the opening of the centre in the central feature at the junction of St. David's Way and Town Wall are also of Imperial Mahogany stone. Return to Working Street and cross to the church.

St. John's Church. Much restored and extended, this old parish church is full of geological interest. The original building is of Blue Lias limestone from the Vale of Glamorgan, no doubt shipped from the cliffs of Aberthaw, up the Taff which then ran where Westgate Street stands now, then carted a short distance along Quay and Church Streets to the building. Only the west tower reveals the Lias in its walls however, the rest having been covered by later extensions. Note the rich bivalve debris standing out in section on the Lias blocks, mainly oyster shells.

The dressings of the 1473 Somerset-type tower were of Dundry Stone, but much has been replaced in later restorations. However, the use of this Inferior Oolite stone from the Jurassic beds of an outlier south of Bristol does show an early example of golden oolites reaching Cardiff long before the railway age made the Bath Stones of the Great Oolite so popular.

FIG. 26    Swelldon Stone, a local Carboniferous Limestone, laminated and pinkish tinged. St. John's Church, extensions to north and south aisles.

The Dundry Stone must have been taken by cart down to the Avon, then by ship across the Bristol Channel and so up the Taff to Cardiff's quay. (An even earlier example of the use of Jurassic oolite limestones were the Bath Stone columns of the Roman villa at Trelai Park, the former Cardiff racecourse, excavated by the late Sir Mortimer Wheeler.) It is difficult to tell how much of the dressings on St. John's tower are still of Dundry Stone. Seen close-up, Dundry Stone may be distinguished from Bath Stone because it is mainly formed of fragments of mollusc shells and the comminuted skeletons of corals and algae, whereas Bath Stone is dominantly composed of oolitic grains. However, the two are not mutually exclusive, Dundry Stone may appear oolitic, Bath Stone may have rich shelly debris.

Extensions to St. John's Church in 1886–1897 did not keep tradition with the earlier building by using Blue Lias limestone. Instead the Carboniferous Swelldon limestone was employed. Its slightly pinkish tinge, laminated bedding and round crinoid stems and ossicles easily distinguish it in the north and south aisle walls and in the east end of the church. (A few houses built of it can be seen in Cathedral Road and Cowbridge Road East.) The churchyard wall is of Lias however, with red sandstone coping stones, probably the Devonian Forest of Dean Red.

National & Provincial Building Society, No. 11 Church Street, opposite the tower of St. John's: A new frontage, installed in 1982, bringing another new stone into Cardiff, in the panels below the windows. Its source is not positively identified but it is probably the Bon Accord Red granite from Uthammar in Sweden, an old Precambrian granite from the Baltic Shield which has therefore suffered several phases of deformation. It is coarsely crystalline. The larger pink felspars show signs of crushing, and there is a broad foliation which indicates that the rock is approaching a gneiss in type. Proceed southwards along Trinity Street.

Cardiff Central Library. A Pennant Sandstone plinth is surmounted by a building faced in Bath Stone, the Corsham Down variety from West Wiltshire. The main entrance steps are of porphyritic Cornish granite (Hercynian age), with felspar phenocrysts set in a groundmass of quartz and mica. Built in stages, the last addition to this building was the 1896 south frontage, facing The Hayes. Here the tradition of the earlier sections was broken with, firstly in the white columns of the central area which are of Portland Stone, and secondly, a piece of good fortune for geologists, in the relief panels high up on either side, for these are of Ham Hill Stone, the sandy limestone from the Jurassic Inferior Oolite, quarried near Monta-

FIG. 27    Cardiff Central Library, south frontage facing The Hayes. Bath Stone with Portland Stone columns and panels of Ham Hill Stone high up on either side.

FIG. 28   Larvikite columns & travertine porch below the Portland Stone eastern
frontage of David Morgan's store, The Hayes.

cute in Somerset. This deep-golden stone can be recognised by the deep weathering of its cross-bedded structures. The panels can now be seen more readily from the higher balconies of the St. David's Hall opposite.

Cross the Hayes to Milward's shoe shop below the corner of Oxford House. Fine shop front panels of light-green brecciated and white-veined marble from Tinos in the Aegean Sea have recently been ripped out here. This is a good vantage point for the group of buildings on the west side of the Hayes, making up the David Morgan department store.

David Morgan. 1904 section: Grey Forest of Dean Stone with Bath Stone dressings. Rough walls in Pennant Sandstone with courses of Red Forest of Dean Stone between floors. 1899 section: White Portland Stone, red sandstone and Bath Stone. Granite columns to the first floor. 1912 section: Portland Stone with columns of larvikite, particularly the lower part. Across the whole frontage there is a porch of Roman travertine, while the ground floor of the 1912 section has one of the priceless geological treasures of Cardiff, four great solid columns of larvikite! Note the Forest of Dean Red sandstone. This is of Devonian (Brownstones) age, from the Wilderness Quarry at Mitcheldean. Sometimes also known as Red Wilderness, it is a hard medium-grained stone, 89 per cent silica and with good weathering properties.

Enter Hill Street and walk along to the Tesco Store. A pleasing addition to the brickmaking materials used in Cardiff, it is built of Wealden brick from the Cretaceous Wealden Beds of S.E. England. Spots of black in the bricks come from the minute particles of manganese in the clay beds. The notable feature of the brick is its warmth and variety of interest.

# TRAIL 4:

# DUKE STREET – HIGH STREET – ST. MARY STREET – WESTGATE STREET

Duke Street Arcade, 1902, is faced with grey Forest of Dean stone from Bixslade. No. 2 Duke Street, A.G. Meek's shoe shop, has panels of brecciated red serpentinite, a beautiful stone known as Rosso Levante from Levanto in Liguria, Italy. At least four important geological events have contributed to the history of such a stone – its primary formation, its metamorphism to serpentinite, then brecciation and, finally, its re-cementing. Enter High Street, east side.

*High Street*

Williams and Glyn's Bank, No. 2, has a superb facade in the dark Emerald Pearl larvikite from Norway. At Laura Ashley, No. 5, notice the Bath Stone portico above which is one of Cardiff's first banks, built in 1835. Bowes and Bowes, No. 6, and High & Mighty, No. 7, have panels of larvikite and Tinos marble respectively.

The best new facades in the French Napoleon Tigre marble from Hydrequent in the Pas de Calais form the frontage of Pizzaland/Mister Nudge, Nos. 8–10. They show superb sedimentary laminations and areas of broken algal and mud-flake debris. Some of the clear calcite occurs as veins which cross the bedding. (N.B. the bedding has been fixed vertically in some of the panels.) These veins are due to drying-out and shrinkage cracks, rather than lines of stress due to subsequent deformation.

Holland & Barrett, No. 11, larvikite surround. Watches of Switzerland, No. 12, a fine dark-green brecciated serpentinite of unknown origin, particularly well seen on the side at the entrance to High Street Arcade, the entrance also having (high overhead) columns of pink Peterhead granite. Courts, No. 14, on the opposite side of the arcade entrance has large panels of red and green brecciated serpentinite, the Rosso Levante. Cross Church Street and enter St. Mary Street.

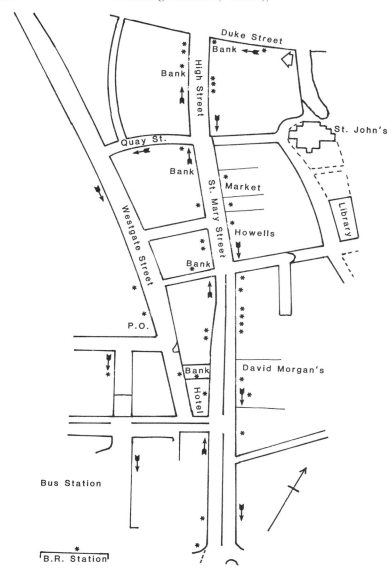

FIG. 29   Route Map for Trail 4.

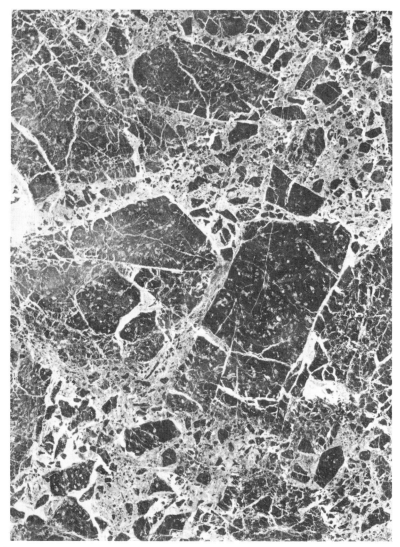

FIG. 30   The Italian red brecciated serpentinite, Rosso Levante, at Courts Furnishers, High Street.

*St. Mary Street*

Market Buildings, 1886, with Stead & Simpson, market entrance and H. Samuel below. Plinths of pink Peterhead granite with flat columns of grey porphyritic Cornish granite above, with large felspar phenocrysts. Further pink and fine-grained grey granite columns occur on all floors of the facade above. The second-floor bay window above the market entrance arch has a course of Radyr Stone Triassic breccia beneath it. All the other window columns and supports are in Bath Stone. Note the Formica imitation marble below the windows of H. Samuel!

Borough Arms. Bath Stone building with pink granite columns on all floors, but notice the squares of Barge Quartzite, a metamorphic rock from Monte Bracco in the Italian Western Alps which appear above the name.

Howells store is faced in Portland Stone on the ground and first floors, but with Bath Stone and stucco on the third and fourth. Panels of a dark-green serpentinite breccia marble frame one of the shop doorways. This is the Verde Alpi from the Val d'Aosta, Italian Alps. Cross the entrance to Wharton Street.

The Cheltenham & Gloucester Building Society, No. 20, has light blue larvikite and a fine dark-grey slate with evidence of bedding. Notice the sidewall in Wharton Street, where the bedding is particularly well seen. It is picked out by original variations in grain size and crosses the panels which have therefore been cut along the cleavage. This is the Silurian Burlington slate from quarries at Kirkby in Furness, on the hills of the Lake District overlooking the Duddon Estuary.

The Sandringham (Doogal's Restaurant), No. 21. The pinnacles and depths of British marble work are joined together in this building, for another Formica imitation faces the street on the north side of the facade, but behind it the entrance porch and a panel facing the street on the south side are lined with Ashburton marble. This Middle Devonian limestone from Ashburton in Devon is no longer worked. Its mottled light and dark-grey colours are due to its fossil content. Brachiopods and stromatoporoids predominate, but there is also crinoid debris and tabulate corals such as *Heliolites*, *Favosites*, *Pachypora* and *Thamnopora cervicornis*. Thus Ashburton marble gives us a picture of a Devonian reef from 375 million years ago when

FIG. 31   The Middle Devonian Ashburton marble with light grey mottling due to brachiopods and stromatoporoids and red and white calcite veining. Porch of The Sandringham, St. Mary Street.

Britain lay south of the Equator. The rock is criss-crossed by veins of calcite, some reddened from iron staining which was derived from New Red Sandstone deposits, Permo-Triassic, once overlying the Ashburton district. The marble is not metamorphosed, i.e. it is not a true marble and thus not good for exposed external situations. Notice how the panels are much better preserved within the porch. Many British marbles are similar; i.e. they are dense limestones, capable of taking a high polish, but can only retain it when used in interiors.

Continuing down the street, Crouch, No. 22 has light blue larvikite; K. Shoes, No. 24, white Carrara marble with grey veins; Nationwide Building Society, No. 26, above the ground floor, panels of dark-grey slate which need to be seen at close quarters but from pavement level reveal some fossil evidence suggesting the Devonian grey slate from Delabole in Cornwall; No. 28, Carrara marble with grey veins and patches; Louis Restaurant, No. 32, light blue larvikite. Examine the entrance to the Les Croupiers casino. Here the steps are in the striking black and gold-veined Portoro marble dug near Portovenere on the Gulf of Spezia, Italy. Variously described in the stone-trade

literature as Fortor, Fortoro and Port Oro, this marble is
derived from black, rather siliceous limestone. It was fractured
by tectonic movement and the fissures were then filled with
calcite, which has been stained golden-brown by iron oxide.

Western frontage of the David Morgan store. 1896 frontage:
windows framed with 'black granite'. First to third floors in
Grey and Red Forest of Dean stones, and at the top, bands of
another rarity in Cardiff, the deep-yellow Guiting Stone from
the Inferior Oolite of the Cotswolds. 1898 frontage: (ground
floor matches the other frontage and also includes Carmelle
and Noa Noa premises) Grey Forest of Dean stone, red Devonian Old Red Sandstone and North Staffordshire Triassic sandstone. The terracotta work is from the Cattybrook works near
Almondsbury, Avon. This works, in an inlier of Carboniferous
beds, supplied great quantities of terracotta and machine-
pressed brick to Cardiff, and is still in work.

Below the windows of Lears, No. 37, there are panels of a
green serpentinite, probably Polcevera from Italy, and after
crossing the entrance to Royal Arcade there is a *conglomerato*
version of the same stone lining the doorway to the Incognito
Club.

Beautiful blocks of polished Cornish granite, probably from
Bodmin Moor or Penryn, appear in the wall of S.A. Brain's
offices, their felspars showing alignment and indicating their
late growth in the Hercynian-aged granite melt. At the south
end of the street cross to the west side and return northwards.

The Great Western Hotel (c.1875–9) is one of the best
examples of the random polygonal-jointed walling in Cardiff,
carried out in local pink-stained (i.e. slightly hematised) Carboniferous Limestone. The dressings are of Bath Stone. Walking north, the south end of the Philharmonic building, No. 68,
the former Western Mail Offices, displays an enormous decorative arch extending up four floors in polished pink Peterhead
granite. Cross Wood Street.

Royal Hotel. This hotel has a ground floor of Portland Stone
with pink Peterhead granite columns, the floors above being
finished in Bath Stone with flat columns of the same granite.

Lloyds Bank, No. 89, has an unpolished grey granite base
with Portland Stone above. The porch has an inner frame of
polished red granite, probably the Balmoral variety from Finland. The outer frame is of polished grey granite from Bess-

brook, Northern Ireland. The four red granite columns of the semi-circular porch canopy are of a different stone than the door frame and appear to be a Swedish Precambrian granite. When the bank is open examine the interior entrance walls. They are of orange-red Rosso Verona marble, faults in the stone accounting for the apparent pink veins which are spaces infilled with resins.

The premises of Dollond & Aitchison, No. 90, have a grey fine-grained granite frame with an outer frame of dark larvikite, while Westminster House has a facade of Portland Stone and brick. Cross the entrance to Golate.

Below the Bank of Ireland, No. 106, there is another welcome recent introduction to Cardiff, a plinth of red Aptian (Lower Cretaceous) marble, full of large white rudistid and other smaller brachiopods. From Spain, but known to the Italian stone trade as Rosso Biulbo, the examples here are continued along the frontage of Elgin House, the former Queens Hotel, where the entrance porch steps are another example of a *conglomerato*. The facades of the building above, and over the premises of Forward Trust, are Bath Stone with columns of Staffordshire New Red Sandstones.

FIG. 32 Cornish (Hercynian) granite with aligned felspar phenocrysts; S.A. Brain's office frontage, St. Mary Street.

FIG. 33   The Great Western Hotel, a fine example of random polygonal jointing in the Kentish Ragstone style, carried out in Carboniferous limestone with Bath Stone dressings.

FIG. 34   Rudistid brachiopods in red Lower Cretaceous (Aptian) marble from Spain. Allied Irish Bank, St. Mary Street.

A light green serpentinite marble used on the frontage of the Bristol and West Building Society, No. 108, has relatively small blocks, not much brecciated. It is possibly the Verde Aver from Italy. Next door at the Services Careers Office there is an Italian buff marble known as Ondagata, of unknown provenance but revealing wavy lines suggesting origin from a nodular limestone, and some conglomeratic bands. Cross the entrance to Guildhall Place.

The Midland Bank/Commercial Bank of Wales Building, formerly the Co-op building, is another example of a Portland Stone clad building, standing on a plinth of Forest of Dean Grey Stone. More Portland Stone facings can be seen further up St. Mary Street at the extension to the National Westminster and Trustee Savings Banks. Re-enter High Street.

The entrance to Castle Arcade is panelled in mottled, white-veined serpentinite marble, with the Clive Ranger shop on the north side displaying salmon pink *conglomerato* panels of limestone fragments.

Lloyds Bank, No. 27, has grey granite around the doorway, displaying swirling mixtures of dark and light granite, some of the patches being xenoliths; probably the Bessbrook granite from Northern Ireland. Thos. Cook, No. 28 and Jaeger, No. 29, are clad in white Carrara marble and a frame of grey granite with Portland Stone above, respectively. Return to Quay Street and walk west into Westgate Street.

## Westgate Street

Westgate Street stands on the old course of the River Taff. The river was diverted when Cardiff Central Station was built, and the reclaimed ground was filled in with surplus stone from the ballast bank at the docks. The surrounding land was then developed as Temperance Town, covering the area where the rugby ground, Post and Telecom buildings, Western Mail & Echo Offices and the Empire Pool now stand. Walk south down Westgate Street to the Inland Revenue Offices, 1904, a fine facade of Portland Stone which is continued in the Post Office adjacent on the south side.

The granite details of the Post Office are another outstanding geological feature of Cardiff. The doorways are lined with Shap granite, an adamellite granite from early Devonian age intrusions, quarried on Wasdale Crag in the Lake District. The rock is distinctive for its large pink orthoclase felspars set in the red groundmass of quartz, orthoclase and oligoclase in equal proportions, together with some biotite (black mica). It is a truly porphyritic granite. Small amounts of accessory minerals are present, such as sphene, apatite and magnetite, but these are not detectable by visual examination.

The contrast in size between the pink orthoclase phenocrysts and the other mineral grains in this stone is evidence of the multi-phase cooling history of the Shap granite melt, as it was introduced into the earth's crust. Under angled light the felspars reveal a single twinning plane. Clots, known as 'Heathen' to the quarrymen, are xenoliths, probably relics of an earlier intrusion caught up in the arrival of the new melt. Shap granite occurs in Red (Dark) and Grey (Light) varieties, but these are not separate intrusions. The main mass is grey granite, the red occurring as ribs, half to five metres in width on either side of master joints. The more persistent the joint, the more of the Red variety around it.

The main entrance to the Post Office is flanked with polished columns of grey Aberdeen granite, while on the third floor above and in the north and south pavilions there are columns of a darker grey Bessbrook granite, of Caledonian (Old

FIG. 35   Red variety Shap Granite with large pink felspar phenocrysts, Westgate Street Post Office doorways.

Red Sandstone) age, from the base of Camlough west of Newry in Northern Ireland. The roofing slates of the Post Office are Westmorland Slate, Ordovician, quarried on the slopes of Coniston Old Man in the Lake District.

Cross to the rear entrance to Lloyds Bank, St. Mary Street Branch, described earlier on this trail. It has been given the same handsome treatment as the front facade. The light grey granite of the lower walls is particularly fine (Carnsew, West Cornwall?). Walk west along Park Street to the Western Mail & Echo offices. The capping to the low boundary wall of the entrance car park is of highly fossiliferous Jurassic oolitic limestone, probably from the Forest marble.

Cross Wood Street and the Bus Station to Cardiff Central Station, B.R. The station has good porphyritic granite slabs as a plinth course, with the aligned felspar phenocrysts suggesting flow in the late stages of the cooling of the granite melt. The granite is of Bodmin Moor type. In the main booking hall, the columns are decorated with flat slabs of Kitley green marble from the Devonian limestones near Yealmpton, Devon. The rock is limestone capable of taking a high polish in interior work. It is not a true metamorphosed marble.

FIG. 36   Kitley green marble from Yealmpton, Devon. A middle Devonian limestone. Cardiff Central Station booking hall.

The green limestone has veins of reddened and white calcite, some of which have opened up slightly or 'feathered', i.e. not polished to a smooth finish. Unfortunately the slabs have been overpainted with a varnish which has left brush marks across the grain of the marble and allowed people to scratch names on the varnish coating. The marble is no longer worked so it has a rarity value and should certainly be preserved. (The same stone adorns the internal entrance archway of the Geological Museum, London.)

# TRAIL 5:

# CARDIFF CASTLE (EXTERIOR) AND CATHAYS PARK

The trail commences at the main gate of the castle in Duke Street. Cardiff Castle stands on the site of three previous wood-built Roman forts. In their fourth fortification of the site the Romans turned to the use of stone, and, good engineers as they were, rejected the rounded river cobbles of the immediate site, for these do not engage well in walls. They require much plaster to hold them. The plaster is liable to admit a lot of water, and as a result the walls may collapse in frosty weather. The Romans preferred the easily laid and evenly-bedded durable Blue Lias limestones. Tradition has it that they quarried this stone at the foot of Leckwith Hill, but it is far more likely that it was obtained from the Aberthaw cliffs and sailed up the Taff to be landed on the river bank hard by the fort. The Roman walls later fell into disrepair and were robbed for the building of the Norman keep which can be glimpsed through the main gateway. A great earth bank was then thrown over the remaining Roman work and a stockade built on top. Thus, the Roman remnants were hidden until restoration at the end of the nineteenth century. Then the bank was removed, the Roman work uncovered, and the present walls built over it, on exactly the same foundations. This work extended into the 1920s. Surviving fragments of the Roman wall can be seen on the outside of the castle at the eastern end of the south frontage. To clearly mark the Roman work, a course of Radyr Stone was laid over the top, thus separating it visually from the Carboniferous Limestone used in the rebuilding above – a refinement hardly necessary for the geologist!

Examine the walls west of the main gate. Obviously later than the Roman work, here the rounded river cobbles are predominant and all the likely materials brought down by the River Taff are represented, Pennant, Millstone Grit and Old Red Sandstone. The clock tower at the south-west corner is a William Burges addition during the nineteenth century restoration. A dominant feature of the Cardiff skyline, it is built of Forest of Dean Stone known as Mine Train. This durable sand-

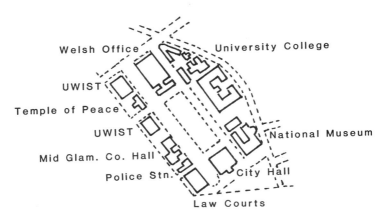

Welsh Office
University College
UWIST
Temple of Peace
UWIST
National Museum
Mid Glam. Co. Hall
Police Stn.
City Hall
Law Courts

FIG. 37    Location of principal buildings in Cathays Park, Trail 5.

FIG. 38    Lias limestone remnants of the Roman fort in the base of Cardiff Castle walls, with courses of Red Radyr Stone breccia to mark this work off from the Carboniferous limestone parts above.

stone varies in colour from blue-grey to reddish tinged, and is again from the Bixslade area. Less important sandstone work at the castle was supplied from the Marquis's own quarry at Pwll y pant, north of Caerphilly.

Walk along the frontage to the south-east corner. East of the main gate the walls above the Roman fragments are of a pinkish-tinged limestone which is probably the Swelldon Stone from former quarries near Culverhouse Cross, but a dramatic change occurs near the south-east corner where the Creigiau/Pentyrch limestone takes over. It is deeper in tone, yellowish-brown and pinkish tinged, being slightly hematised and iron-stained. The turrets above are capped with red standstones.

A fragment of the Blue Lias limestone-built town wall stands as a buttress to the sloping flower bed near the south-east corner. Walk north to the subway, a former tunnel of the Glamorgan Canal and cross to the Rose & Crown opposite, behind which there is another wall on the alignment of the old town wall, again of Lias limestone, and probably the medieval walls were built by robbing more of the existing Lias buildings nearby. After the dissolution of the monasteries the Greyfriars Monastery was another quarry for Lias stone. The material was used in buildings in the present Queen Street area.

Walk north-eastwards towards the Prudential Building and the entrance to Greyfriars. The Portland Stone ashlar-faced council offices on the north side of Greyfriars have panels of Lakeland Green Slate below their windows and plinth courses of 'black granite'. The plinth of Devonshire House is of black granite from Zimbabwe, while those of the county council offices between it and the New Theatre are of Doulting Stone, the Inferior Oolite limestone from Somerset which is used in Wells Cathedral.

From Greyfriars cross northwards under the Boulevard de Nantes, turning left at the far end to the south frontage of the Law Courts, 1904. All the buildings of Cathays Park, Cardiff's famous civic centre, are faced with Portland Stone. It has long been a favourite in public buildings, its pure white colour making them appear more imposing.

However, despite the uniformity of the building stones used, there are many details of geological interest, particularly in the statues and memorials and in the richly-decorated interiors of some of the buildings. On the lawn south of the Law Courts the memorial to Gwilym Williams of Miskin is of unpolished Grey variety Shap granite. The felspars are still pink, it is the groundmass which is different in colour.

FIG. 39   Cardiff City Hall; in Portland Stone. The statue of Lord Tredegar in the foreground stands on a plinth of Carboniferous Darley Dale gritstone from Derbyshire.

Walk east towards the City Hall, 1904. The memorial to the South African Wars at the south end of Edward VII Avenue, now a small roundabout, is of unpolished pink Peterhead granite. The boundary of the Law Court and City Hall lawns is edged with grey granite but the pillars are of Portland Stone. Some of these display fine weathering-out of shell fragments, a measure of erosion since 1904, e.g. the first one west of the City Hall entrance (Polish War Memorial) where shell debris is particularly evident at eye level and in the upper part. It is worth trying to see the interior of the City Hall. On the first floor is the magnificent Marble Hall, a rich gold and white blend of Italian and Greek stones. The statues are of the Serevezza marble, the best white from the Carrara–Massa district, but their plinths are of Pentelic marble from Mount Pentelikon in Attica, Greece. The gold-coloured stone is the magnificent Siena marble from Tuscany. The Council Chamber has two great columns of Italian Paonazzo marble, white with purplish-greenish veins.

Walk onto the lawns in front of the City Hall. The statue of Lord Tredegar (Balaclava), 1909, by Goscombe John near the Boulevard de Nantes is on a base of very fine siliceous, buff-coloured and evenly-grained gritstone, the Carboniferous (Millstone Grit) Darley Dale Stone quarried around the Derwent Valley NW of Matlock. This example is from the Stancliffe quarries and is 96 per cent silica.

Move to the Gorsedd Gardens in front of the National Museum of Wales. Laid out in 1909, these gardens contain a Gorsedd circle of standing stones in Radyr Stone breccia. The beds are set up on end and some show the plug and feathers drill marks of the quarrymen. West of the circle the statue of Lord Ninian Edward Crichton Stuart, MP, 1915, is on a fine-grained non-porphyritic granite, while to the south that of John Cory, 1906, is of Portland Stone on a plinth of Derbyshire gritstone and brick. David Lloyd George, facing the National Museum of Wales, stands atop Portland Stone as well. Surely it should have been Welsh slate?

The superb steps of the Museum are built of Cornish granite, of Bodmin Moor type, porphyritic with medium-size felspar phenocrysts, and were built 1929–1932. (The interior is mainly lined with fossil and stylolite-rich Portuguese marble.) The majority of the other buildings in Cathays Park have Carboniferous gritstone steps.

FIG. 40   The Gorsedd circle in Radyr Stone, a Triassic desert breccia, with the Portland Stone facade of the National Museum of Wales beyond.

Grey slate panels (Dolemaen?) adorn the most recently built part of the Main Building of University College, the S.E. corner facing Park Place, and reveal rusty-weathering brown pyrite nodules. For those who can visit the interior of the building, the main staircase is lined with gypsum panels, the only known use in a Cardiff building of gypsum or alabaster from the local Triassic outcrops in the cliffs south of Penarth. (In contrast to the similar deposits on the opposite coast of the Bristol Channel at Blue Anchor, the Penarth deposits were not generally suitable for ornamental purposes, making lamp stands, ash trays, &c.) In the entrance hall there is a statue of Viriamu Jones in the best white statuary marble from Serevezza, Italy, mounted on a plinth of orange-veined Arabescato variety, situated above steps edged with an interestingly-figured but so far unidentified green marble.

The Police Station, 1968, on Edward VII Avenue has a course of metamorphic skifer stone at pavement level below its Portland Stone claddings. Before leaving the south end of Cathays Park walk up Edward VII Avenue. The UWIST Bute Building is roofed with two North Wales slates, silver grey from Dolemaen and blue from Portmadog. The Temple of Peace beyond is another building with a very rich interior. Permission must be sought to see it. The entrance hall is paved with the marble Meureil from Villiers les Hauts, Yonne, France, with borders of golden travertine and black marble, and its walls are lined with buff-coloured Larrys marble from Ravieres et Cry, Yonne, France, in which brachiopod shells can be seen. Meureil and Larrys are both Jurassic. The great hall of the temple has similar flooring to the entrance hall, in travertine, most of it being the creamy Roman or Sicilian type. The strips of the deep golden variety may also be Italian, but this colour is also quarried at Cannstadt near Stuttgart in Germany and in Czechoslovakia. The notable features of the main hall are the superb fluted columns of Portoro black and gold marble from Portovenere near La Spezia, Liguria, Italy. The walls of the hall are lined with the gently-banded Trani Mirabelle marble, probably Cretaceous in age; from Bari, Italy.

FIG. 41  Portland Roach with cavities of dissolved fossils, including an example of the Calcareous red alga, *Solenopora*.

Cross the avenue to the new extension to the Welsh Office. The extension is a geological must, for it makes extensive use of the Portland Stone Roach. This cavity-rich material is employed all round the building in the sloping base and carried up the centre of the columns onto the overhanging floors above as a relief to the large surfaces of Portland Stone proper. Very large colonies of the red alga *Solenopora* and cavities once occupied by *Aptyxiella Portlandica* and *Laevitrigonia* species are a feature of the stone. The fossils were dissolved out because they were originally of the unstable form of calcium carbonate, the mineral aragonite.

# TRAIL 6:

# BUTE STREET – WEST BUTE STREET – MOUNT STUART SQUARE

This trail starts well out on the old marshlands of Cardiff, by the Old Bute Street station. Much of the marshland around this area was filled in with ballast stones from the ballast bank of the earlier Glamorgan Canal, a bank which grew to over a quarter mile in length on more than on occasion.

Pascoe House is the first building on the left, notable for its courses of Radyr Stone along the ground floor, in the entrance steps and, in alternative blocks with Bath Stone, in the ground floor window arches. The stone is dominated by limestone clasts. The Bath Stone of the building is intricately carved and shows how detailed work could be carried out on the better varieties such as the Box Ground. There are short dark-grey columns of Bessbrook granite, evenly-grained with small squarish felspars, by the doorway.

Walk down to a point opposite the imposing frontage of the National Westminster Bank. This is one of the best Portland facades in Cardiff and is matched identically at the other end of the building in West Bute Street. As at Marments, sections in the columns reveal the maximum depth obtainable from the beds. Floors three and four above have been weathered since the building was erected in 1929 and numerous cavities have opened up where *Laevitrigonia* and *Aptyxiella* occurred in the stone. Some blocks are consequently approaching the condition of the Roach in texture. The frontage has a plinth of Cornish granite. The interior is another of Cardiff's gems.

The walls begin with a plinth of rich black marble of unknown origin (the Carboniferous beds from Galway were renowned for the density of their black polish). The walls above and the splendid fluted columns of the banking hall are recorded as Echaillon marble from the Isère region of the French Alps near Grenoble. The main walls do not seem much different from polished Portland Stone in colour and figuration. However, the fluted columns are certainly foreign in origin and must be the Echaillon material. The creamy-coloured stone

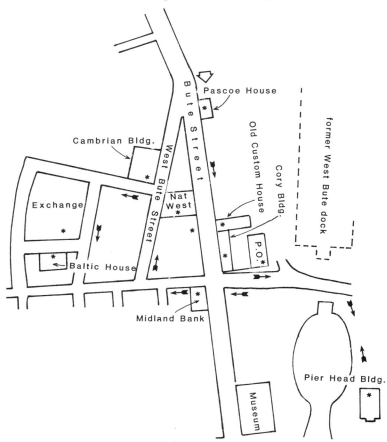

FIG. 42   Route Map for Trail 6.

contains many fossils preserved in grey calcite, mainly oyster species, and there are many stylolites due to pressure solution.

Many buildings in Cardiff stand on unconsolidated drift deposits. The southern part of the City Centre and all the Bute Street/Docks area has a thick cover of recent drift, river and marsh deposits. Building records of the National Westminster Bank show that concrete piling to a depth of 10–12m was necessary to establish a concrete sub-frame for the structure.

Another good example of measurable weathering occurs in the old Custom House on the east side of Bute Street. Built of

FIG. 43   Pascoe House, Bute Street, a facade with extensive use of Radyr Stone.

Portland Stone in 1898, the shell debris is now standing proud of the ground floor blocks.

Note the green Polcevera marble *conglomerato* around the entrance to Mel's Club opposite. The marble comes from Pontedecimo north of Genoa, Liguria, Italy, and is an ophicalcite, calcite veins cementing a brecciated serpentinite. Continue south to the Cory Building. It is built of Bath Stone on a dressed but unpolished plinth of porphyritic granite. Around the corner in Bute Crescent, the Post Office, 1881, formerly the Mercantile & Telegraph Building, is a fine example of a red sandstone building, very fine-grained and evenly-bedded, with cross-bedding structures visible to the right of the posting box. The source of the stone has not been identified. It may be the deep red St. Bees sandstone (Triassic) from Cumbria, and it is fine to medium grain, with angular and sub-angular quartz cemented by silica and with some white mica present. The columns to the facade and porch of the building are of fine-grained granite. Walk inside the dock gate for a view of the 1896 Pier Head Building. Although mainly of brick and terracotta, it does contain examples of granite as well as Grey and Red Forest of Dean Stone.

On the opposite side of Bute Street, the Midland Bank has an intricately decorated building with many columns of pink

Peterhead granite, those on the ground floor standing on plinths of grey granite. The pink columns contain several examples of xenoliths, the darker patches caused by imperfectly absorbed roof material which fell into the intruding granite melt. In this rock the xenoliths are usually of Dalradian Schist material. There are elaborate dressings of Bath Stone and terracotta, with the upper floors carried out in yellow brick.

From this bank walk west along James Street and turn first right into West Bute Street. Proceed to the Western frontage of the National Westminster Bank, already described. Opposite, on the corner between West Bute Street and the entrance to Mount Stuart Square, stands the fine Cambrian/Cymric House building in the Corsham Down variety of Bath Stone, quarried from underground sources close to the Box railway tunnel in West Wiltshire. Erected in 1918, the building is another which required foundation piling to a depth of 9m.

Walk west into Mount Stuart Square. Bath and Portland Stones predominate. The Coal Exchange Building in the centre of the square is faced with Corsham Down stone. Opened in 1886 and added to again up to 1900, this was another site with foundation problems. Alluvial mud 9m thick 'of the consistency of butter' was recorded by the contractors, who could not excavate it because of the danger to nearby buildings and had to solve the problem by digging shafts to gravels below. These were then filled with concrete, and a series of arches built on them to carry the building. The site was further complicated by the old slag pits of the Cardiff glassworks which had occupied the site some 50 years previously.

Opposite the south frontage of the Exchange stands Baltic House, with a wonderful entrance frame in polished deep-red granite from Grafverfors or Vanevik in Sweden. Note the blue quartzes which confirm that this is the Virgo granite, of Precambrian age. Slight crushing of the quartzes at a later stage has given them internal reflecting planes. Some are of a delicate opalescent blue. The entrance porch is lined internally with Roman travertine, which in this instance has been stopped in with a black resin to give a contrasting effect.

FIG. 44   Entrance porch to Baltic House, Mount Stuart Square. Superb frame of red granite, with interior lining in black resin filled travertine panels.

# TRAIL 7:
# LLANDAFF AND THE CATHEDRAL

The trail starts at the entrance to Spencers Row in Bridge Street north of the Cathedral Green. Seen through the archway, the cottages of Spencers Row are an excellent example of the Radyr Stone, and there are many other houses built of or with courses of this Triassic desert deposit in the Llandaff area, for the quarry was close by.

Walk south towards the Cathedral Green. The 1914–18 War Memorial with its three bronze figures standing towards the back of the green is of the Grey Shap variety of granite. Move south again to the ruins of the thirteenth century bell-tower. It is faced with Blue Lias limestone from the Glamorgan cliffs, no doubt carried up the Taff to the site. Rubble fill behind the Lias facing incorporates all the earlier building materials of the cathedral, e.g. Radyr Stone, Dundry Stone and river cobbles.

FIG. 45   Triassic Radyr Stone and Carboniferous sandstone; the lych gate, Llandaff.

On the grass in front of the bell-tower there is another memorial stone in the Grey Shap granite. To the south note the Lias limestones again in the remains of the Bishop's palace.

Walk to the lych gate and the paths leading down to the west front. The lych gate is built in Radyr Stone and Grey Forest of Dean Stone and the wall leading down to the cathedral is all of Radyr Stone. Examine the clasts in the Radyr Stone on the way down. Across the lane from it, a retaining wall of river cobbles is worthy of note.

Llandaff Cathedral contains examples of several stones not recognised elsewhere on these trails. Like the oldest parts of St. John's in the City Centre, its earlier fabric incorporates Dundry Stone and a good deal of Blue Lias. Three building eras have been identified in the stonework of the cathedral – firstly, that of the marginal Lias facies, the Sutton Stone from the Ogmore/Southerndown area, associated with the Norman or 'Urban' church and probably combined with Radyr Stone or immediately abundant river cobbles. Then, an era of Dundry Stone used in alterations and extensions to Urban's church during the thirteenth century. Thirdly, still in the thirteenth century, the era of the Blue Lias limestones. We may add a fourth era, the nineteenth century restoration which brought in many new varieties of golden Jurassic stones – from Combe Down, from Chipping Camden and Clipsham, Monk's Park and Hartham Park (both near Corsham in Wiltshire) and smaller amounts of Doulting Stone from Somerset; Beer Stone from East Devon; Portland Stone from Dorset; Hornton Stone, a Liassic stone from Oxfordshire, and some Hopton Wood Stone from Derbyshire. The cathedral has, of course, much white statuary marble from Carrara, but it also adds a new foreign sedimentary stone to the list seen on these trails, the Caen Stone from near Calvados in Normandy. (Several other city churches have details in Caen Stone.)

Clearly, the exterior of the cathedral can be viewed by geological groups, but the interior should be respected as more suited to individual study. Start at the west front.

The central wall of the west front is of Dundry Stone (Inferior Oolite, Jurassic), from south of Bristol, no doubt sailed up the Taff to be landed on the bank hard by. Of granular appearance, the stone becomes paler with weathering and may eventually become grey, or in sheltered sites, so coated with dirt that it appears black.

The tower to the left, the north-west or Jasper Tower of 1485, is a Blue Lias limestone tower of Somerset type, remarkably like that of St. John's Church, with pinnacles of Bath Stone which were restored in the last century. To the left of the west door at the junction of the tower with the Dundry Stone of the West wall, notice some blocks of Sutton Stone, about 1.2m up in the wall. Probably re-used from the earlier Urban church, these are of the conglomeratic near-shore facies of the Liassic sea and were formed around an archipelago of islands of Carboniferous Limestone strung across the present Vale of Glamorgan area. The clasts inside are therefore beach pebbles of Carboniferous Limestone. Like Dundry Stone, Sutton Stone is a freestone, i.e. it can be cut and sawn in any direction. It is much coarser in texture however, uneven in grain, and its dressed surfaces are rougher. Like many stones it hardens on exposure. The Blue Lias limestone beds of the tower are of much better quality than those to be seen later in the Chapter House. The plinths and buttresses have certainly been renewed and are dressed with Hartham Park variety Bath Stone, while renewed parapet and belfry windows are in the Monk's Park type. York Stone flagstones display parting lineation in the paved approach to the west door.

It is useful to the geologist to know the age of building works as this can give a measure of the strength and durability of a stone. The south-west tower with its tall spire is of much later age, being a rebuilding of an ancient tower which collapsed. The rebuilding took place in the nineteenth century, when the base was constructed of re-used Dundry Stone. The upper part of the tower brought in the Inferior Oolite stone from Chipping Camden, and more recent restoration of the top of the spire has been carried out in Clipsham Stone from near Stamford in Rutland. Chipping Camden Stone is distinguished by its yellow colour and the weathered alignments along its surfaces, whereas Clipsham Stone is a warm-looking, rather coarse-grained shelly limestone. It is a pity that these stones are inaccessible and that Llandaff does not have a display of its building stones as is now the case in some other cathedrals, e.g. Ely.

Walk around to the south side of the building, the retaining wall on the right of the path is of Radyr Stone. The first thing to note on the south side is the magnificent south-west doorway, superb thirteenth century work in Dundry Stone. Some small pieces in the hood moulding of the doorway have later been replaced with the greenish-tinged Rhaetic sandstone, the

Quarella Sandstone, quarried at Bridgend. This stone is white, pale green or grey in colour. It was quarried from three separate beds. A fine-grained rock of quartz and felspar fragments, with a little chert and iron ore, the green colour is due to the presence of chlorite.

Notice the walls above the south-west door. They are typical of the enormous mixture of stones used in this patchwork cathedral – Old Red Sandstones, Lias limestones, and Bath Stone blocks are randomly mixed with river cobbles of Carboniferous sandstone. The buttresses are probably dressed with the Combe Down variety of Bath Stone from just south of Bath itself. The windows have been replaced and reveal another famous Jurassic limestone, the Inferior Oolite Doulting Stone, much used in Wells Cathedral, from east of Shepton Mallet in Somerset. Doulting Stone becomes paler and harder as it weathers, but is a more earthy-looking rock when fresh, and is of a light brown or buff colour. These windows are probably of the Brown Bed or Brambleditch variety in contrast to that of the Welch Regiment Chapel, see below. Overhead, the parapet above the south wall of the nave is of Monk's Park Stone.

The Chapter House, built in the thirteenth century but modified to an octagonal upper structure in the nineteenth, is founded on courses of river cobbles. Above these in its south wall the plinth is of Dundry and Sutton Stone and the latter is also used as dressings to the buttresses. Higher up, a pale pink sandstone is used in the butresses. Examine the Sutton Stone closely. Its cavernous nature could easily be confused with the Portland Roach at a first glance. However, the clasts of darker, Carboniferous Limestone beach pebbles which it contains soon confirm that it is the near-shore Liassic deposit. The main Blue Lias Limestone walls of the Chapter House are of much poorer blocks than those of the Jasper Tower and may well have come from the cliffs between Lavernock and St. Mary's Wells Bay.

The next section of the south wall of the cathedral is the wall to the south choir aisle, again a rich mixture of stones, including a good deal of Radyr Stone breccia. This has also been used in the columns to the doorway, an unfortunate choice as shown by their badly weathered state. The rest of the doorway is of Dundry Stone.

The eastern end of the cathedral, the Lady Chapel, is built of

FIG. 46    Sutton Stone plinth and Blue Lias limestone walls, the Chapter House, Llandaff.

Blue Lias with Bath Stone dressed buttresses and Radyr Stone coming in more frequently below the bases of the windows.

Walk round to the north side where the memorial chapel of the Welch Regiment reflects a time-honoured source of building stones in Cardiff, reverting to the use of river cobbles. The cobbles include the usual mixture of Carboniferous sandstone, Millstone Grit quartz conglomerates and Carboniferous

Limestones, but in the south wall of the chapel there are several quartz conglomerates with red matrixes. These are of the Old Red Sandstone conglomerate. Some quarried Pennant Sandstone lumps occur near the base of the walls. The windows of the chapel are dressed with Doulting Stone, but this is the harder grey variety from the Chelynch or 'Weather-bed' quarry on the north side of the hill at Doulting.

Return to the west front of the cathedral and enter the building. The steps inside, and those inside the south-west door, are of Forest of Dean Red, the Old Red Sandstone from the Wilderness Quarry near Mitcheldean. Note the Dundry Stone arches and columns of the nave. The first three bays on the north side also have much Sutton Stone. Walk to the interior of the south-west door and proceed eastwards along the south aisle. The first effigy in an arch of the south wall is executed in Blue Lias – Henry of Abergavenny, bishop 1193–1228. Continue into the south choir aisle beyond the organ loft. In the last archway on the left, a memorial to one of the cathedral's architects George Gaze Pace incorporates intricately carved fragments of the sedilia, in Caen Stone. The memorial is no tribute to an architect, but the Caen Stone from Calvados in Normandy carves superbly. This creamy-coloured limestone belongs to the same geological horizon as the Bath Stones, i.e. Jurassic Great Oolite, but it does not have an obvious oolitic texture. It was introduced into Britain soon after the Norman Conquest and used up to the fifteenth century. Further examples can be seen in the surviving base of the sedilia on the far side of this wall in the sanctuary, in the reredos to the Lady Chapel and in some memorials in St. Dyfrig's Chapel.

Just beyond the Pace memorial, on the last pier there is a memorial to the 1914–18 war. This is made of Carboniferous Hopton Wood Stone from near Wirksworth in Derbyshire, a shelly coralline limestone full of the fragments of stems and individual ossicles of crinoids. Immediately opposite, on the exterior wall, is another memorial in the same stone, to the Rev. F.W. Edmondes, with a carved surround of pink gypsum. The source of this gypsum may be local but that of the effigy of Lady Audley in the chapel of St. Teilo at the end of the aisle is certainly not. This, and other white alabaster or gypsum effigies in the cathedral, must have come from much better beds at Chellaston, Derbyshire. The local deposits in the Penarth cliffs could never have supplied large white masses of this quality.

Turn left into the Lady Chapel. The entrance steps are in the Red Forest of Dean stone, with edges of Radyr Stone breccia. Opposite is another effigy in the Chellaston gypsum on the tomb of Sir Christopher Matthew. Sadly, the Lady Chapel's former graceful columns of Purbeck marble are no more. They would have been another Cardiff treasure of British marble work, a stone traditionally employed in so many of the cathedrals of Britain.

The magnificent archway between the Lady Chapel and the high altar is superb Norman craftsmanship in the Sutton Stone. Beneath it the polished wall for the candlesticks and the flooring around the altar is carried out in creamy-coloured limestone, absolutely crowded with bivalves. This is polished Purbeck limestone, installed about 1960.

Return to the south aisle and walk back to the doorway into the chancel. Columns of red and green serpentinite adorn its archway and come from the Lizard area, Cornwall. The contrast between the polished and natural appearance of the rock is well seen in the broken column on the left. Bands of black limestone cross the chancel floor, e.g. below the sanctuary step. These are Carboniferous Irish marble, saved from the former high altar paving of the 1860s. Cross the chancel to St. Dyfrig's Chapel opposite. Floor panels here include both Carboniferous gritstones (shot sawn) and Red Forest of Dean stone. Between the chapel and the high altar lie the Matthew and Bishop Ollivant tombs, 1461 and 1882 respectively, the first carried out in white alabaster (gypsum) and the other in Carrara marble. The Ollivant tomb is on a base of carved Caen Stone, with small columns of red and green Cornish serpentinite. On the opposite outer wall of the chapel, another memorial in Caen Stone (to John Nicholl) has a panel of white Carrara marble and twelve small polished columns of hematised limestone, possibly Middle Devonian age beds from Plymouth on account of their similarity to some Plymouth marble in Cardiff Castle.

Walk west through the choir stalls, at both ends of which there are low walls and steps in the same shelly Purbeck limestone from the Swanage quarries used in the high altar paving. Turn right into the north aisle where the chapel of St. Eud-

dogwy contains a marble and alabaster tomb, that of Dean
Vaughan. By the pulpit there is another fine double memorial
in alabaster of the Chellaston type, but, at some time, this
tomb has been re-set on a course of much deeper coloured
material. Beyond, in a double archway set in the north aisle
wall, there are columns of serpentinite and Devonshire marble
around a memorial to Henry Thomas. The black slab of this
memorial is of polished bituminous Carboniferous Limestone.
Several sources existed for Carboniferous Limestone capable of
taking a dense black polish, e.g. the famous quarries near Galway and Kilkenny in Ireland, the Derbyshire Black from near
Ashford, and three types from the Isle of Man – Scarlett Point,
Port St. Mary and Poolvash. It is not easy to distinguish
between any of these without written records. White calcite
figuration here reveals productid brachiopods and the coral
*Syringopora*. Marble inlay, which was so fashionable in Victorian times has been used for the details of the cross in this
memorial. The cross itself is a deep red, probably the Italian
Rosso Rubino or from the French side of the Pyrenees. The
halo is of white Carrara marble, succeeded inwards by triangles
of another red marble, of Carboniferous age, either from Cork
or from Askeaton or Kenney near Limerick. These triangles are
followed by ones of golden Italian Siena marble and around the
intersection of the cross there are more pieces of black marble,
again with fossil corals.

Turn right into the Welch Regiment Chapel. This is entered
by a former external doorway of the cathedral, again of superb
Norman craftsmanship using the marginal Liassic Sutton
Stone. The lectern stands on a base of Beer Stone, the hard
white chalk from the Cretaceous of Beer, near Axminster in
East Devon. This stone was much used for carved church
screens and has a history of working going back to Roman
times. All the dressings of the window and the bases of the columns in the chapel are of Inferior Oolite Doulting Stone from
near Shepton Mallet, but the nature of the stone is rather obs-
cured by the chisel-marking style which has been employed on
it. The base of the priest's desk to the right of the altar is
unusual in that it is of polished Blue Lias limestone, full of the
outlines of fossils, principally the oyster *Gryphaea*. How aptly
named the Blue Lias is!

Leaving the cathedral by the west door, turn right towards

the Prebendal House, and by its entrance right again to the beginning of the Processional Way. Behind the wrought iron entrance gates the doors have a surround and central column of a mottled brown, green and bluish stone, with black and brown vein-like markings. Noted for the variety of colour in a single block, it is the Lower Jurassic (Lias) marble from Hornton in Oxfordshire. The quarries at Hornton have not been worked for some time now however, and it is possible that this stone came from similar deposits quarried just over the Warwickshire border at Edge Hill. The stone is richly fossiliferous.

It is a fitting spot to end these geological trails in Cardiff, for W.D. Conybeare, Dean of Llandaff in 1845, was also a geologist, famous for his studies of Jurassic marine reptiles in another Lias district, the cliffs of Lyme Regis in Dorset.

---

Perhaps these trails will stimulate architects and contractors to further enrich the geology of Cardiff. It would be nice to see examples of, say, the Golden Carioca granite from the Campo Grande in Brazil, the Texas Pink granite from Austin in Texas, the intriguing Norwegian Otta Schist with its foliation and superb lath-like hornblende crystals, and the beautiful nepheline-syenite Foyaite from the Sierra de Monchique in the Algarve, Portugal, and many other fine stones.

# Bibliography

——— Growth of Cardiff 1875–1880. *South Wales Daily News*, 17th January 1880.

——— *Natursten*, Stenindustriens Kontor, Stavern, Norway, 1969.

——— *The Natural Stone Directory*, Stone Industries Journal, 1974.

——— *Buildings of Special Architectural or Historical Interest in Cardiff*, Welsh Office, 1977.

Andrews, John F., *The Story of Solomon Andrews and His Family*, Stewart Williams, 1976.

Ballinger, J. (Ed.) *Cardiff, an Illustrated Handbook*, Western Mail, Cardiff, 1876.

City of Cardiff *Opening of the New City Hall & Law Courts*, Official programme, 29th October 1906.

Clifton-Taylor, Alec *The Pattern of English Building*, Faber, 1972.

Daunton, M.J. Aristocrats & Traders: The Bute Docks, 1839–41. *Jour. Transport History*, 3 (1975) 65–85.

Daunton, M.J. *Coal Metropolis, Cardiff 1870–1914*, Leicester Univ. Press, 1977.

Dutton, G.H. Notes on Glacial & Alluvial Deposits near Cardiff, *Trans. Cardiff Nats. Soc.*, 36 (1903) 108–115.

*Glamorgan, Monmouth & Brecon Gazette*. Shipping movements, various issues, 1832–38.

Hilling, J.B. The Buildings of Cardiff, An Historical Survey, in Stewart Williams' *Glamorgan Historian*, Vol. 6, 1969, Brown, Cowbridge.

Morgan, A.N. *David Morgan, 1833–1919, The Life & Times of a Master Draper in South Wales*, Starling Press, Risca, 1977.

North, F.J. *The Stones of Llandaff Cathedral*, Univ. of Wales Press, 1957.

Perkins, John W. *Geology Explained in South & East Devon*, David & Charles, 1971.

Perkins, J.W., Brooks, A.T. & Pearce, A.E. Mc R, *Bath Stone, A Quarry History*, Kingsmead Press & Department of Extra-mural Studies, Univ. College, Cardiff, 1979.

Shore, B.C.G. *Stones of Britain*, Leonard Hill, London, 1957.

*South Wales Daily News*, various items in issues of 1872–3.

Storrie, John On the Ballast Plants of Cardiff & Neighbourhood, *Trans. Cardiff Nats. Soc.*, 8 (1876) 141–45.

Strahan, A. and Cantrill, T.C., *The Country Around Bridgend*, Mem. Geol. Surv., H.M.S.O., 1904.

Turner, E.W. & Sons *Superb Buildings*, J. Burrow & Co., London, 1929.

Turner, E.W. & Sons 80 Years of Building, *Western Mail*, 31st March 1945.

Turner, E.W. & Sons Histories of Famous Firms, Cardiff Survey, *British Bulletin of Commerce*, 1955.

Wheeler, R.E.M. Roman Buildings & Earthworks on the Cardiff Racecourse, *Transactions Cardiff Nats. Soc.*, 50 (1922) 19–45.

---

Innumerable references to buildings and building stones in Cardiff exist in *The Builder* which has been in publication continuously since 1843. The following are the more important: Volumes 37 (1879) 850–1; 42 (1882) 720; 50 (1886) 268; 56 (1889) 68; 61 (1891) part 2, 30; 66 (1894) part 1, 205, 485; 68 (1895) part 1, 377; 70 (1896) part 1, 560; 72 (1897) part 1, 237–44; 74 (1898) part 1, 191; 95 (1908) part 2, 97; 110 (1916) part 2, 266; 136 (1929) part 1, 324; 155 (1938) part 2, 879–933; 183 (1952) part 2, 298–300; 222 (1972) part 1, 53.

---

Note: the spread of sources indicated by the short, mainly historical bibliography given above is evidence in itself of the haphazard way in which building stones are recorded, and of the need to establish a more adequate record for the future.

# GEOLOGICAL COLUMN

| ERA | PERIOD | | AGE (IN MILLIONS OF YEARS AGO) | BUILDING STONES AVAILABLE FROM |
|---|---|---|---|---|
| CENOZOIC — QUATERNARY | RECENT OR HOLOCENE | | 0. 01 – Present | |
| | PLEISTOCENE | | 1.6–0. 01 | |
| CENOZOIC — TERTIARY | NEOGENE { PLIOCENE / MIOCENE } | | 26 – 1.6 | |
| | PALAEOGENE { OLIGOCENE / EOCENE } | | 65 – 26 | A little limestone. Some puddingstones |
| MESOZOIC | CRETACEOUS | | 140 – 65 | Flints, greenish sandstones |
| | JURASSIC | | 195 – 140 | Many limestones, especially from the Lias (grey), Inferior Oolite and Great Oolite (Bath Stones), golden |
| | TRIASSIC | | 230 – 195 | Red sandstones, some breccias. |
| PALAEOZOIC — UPPER | PERMIAN | | 280 – 230 | Some red sandstones and breccias. |
| | CARBONIFEROUS | | 345 – 280 | Grey sandstones and lime stones. |
| | DEVONIAN | | 395 – 345 | Red sandstones; grey granites, red granites, some slates. |
| PALAEOZOIC — LOWER | SILURIAN | | 435 – 395 | Limestones, greyish; some slates |
| | ORDOVICIAN | | 505 – 435 | Some slates; dolerites. |
| | CAMBRIAN | | 570 – 505 | Purplish, grey and greenish sandstones. Various slates. |
| PRECAMBRIAN | | | 4600 – 570 | Slates |

# BRITISH BUILDING STONES USED IN CARDIFF, CLASSIFIED ACCORDING TO GEOLOGICAL AGE (excluding the interior work of Cardiff Castle where there are several other British marbles).

| | | |
|---|---|---|
| Cretaceous | Beer Stone, flint cobbles. | |
| Jurassic | Purbeck Stone, Purbeck Marble, Portland Roach, Portland Stone.<br>Great Oolite: Bath Stone, Box Ground Stone, Chipping Camden Stone, Corsham Down Stone, Forest Marble, Hartham Park Stone, Monks Park Stone, Ridge Park Stone. | |
| | Inferior Oolite: Clipsham Stone, Doulting Stone, Dundry Stone, Guiting Stone, Ham Hill Stone. | |
| | Lias: Blue Lias, Hornton Stone, Sutton Stone. | |
| Triassic | Rhaetic: Quarella Sandstone. | |
| | Chellaston (Derbs.) gypsum, Corse Hill Stone, Grinshill Stone, N. W. Staffordshire red sandstones, Penarth gypsum, Radyr Stone, St. Bees Sandstone. | |
| Permian | | |
| Carboniferous | Hercynian Orogeny: | De Lank Granite, Fowey Granite (shipping name rather than immediate source), Hantergantink Granite, Penryn Granite. |
| | Coal Measures: Forest of Dean Blue, Forest of Dean Grey, Mine Train Stone, Pennant Sandstones (Newbridge, Pontypridd, Pwll y Pant). | |
| | Millstone Grit: Darley Dale Stone, Derbyshire and York Stone.<br>Carboniferous Limestone: Creigiau, Hopton Wood, Swelldon, Radyr. | |
| Devonian | Ashburton Marble, Forest of Dean Red or Red Wilderness Stone, Kitley green marble, Lizard serpentinite, Old Red Sandstones. | |
| | Caledonian Orogeny: | Aberdeen Granite, Bessbrook Granite, Craigton Granite, Peterhead Granite, Shap Granite. |
| Silurian | Burlington Slate (Furness). | |
| Ordovician | Blaenau Ffestiniog Slates, Lakeland Green Slates, Penmaenmawr Dolerite, Westmorland Slates. | |
| Cambrian | Nantlle Valley Slates. | |
| Precambrian | Uncertain. | |

# Glossary

**Alga** Uni- or multi-cellular fresh or saltwater plant, having chlorophyll and other pigments, but lacking the stems, plants or leaves.

**Arkose** Sandstone containing a notable quantity of felspar grains in addition to the usual quartz.

**Ashlar** Block of hewn and dressed stone with straight edges used in building; of sedimentary rock.

**Augite** Ferromagnesian mineral, pyroxene group, found in basic and ultra-basic volcanic and plutonic igneous rocks.

**Brachiopods** 'Lamp shells'; bivalved shells in which each valve is symmetrical about a central axis, but the two valves are of different shape.

**Breccia** Sedimentary rock type including in it angular fragments of an older rock.

**Calcite** Calcium carbonate mineral.

**Caledonian** Period of mountain building in N.W. Europe centred around late Silurian times.

**Chatter marks** Marks on pebbles due to wave action rolling them about and into each other; percussion marks.

**Clast** Fragment of an older rock embedded in a deposit, e.g. in a breccia or conglomerate.

**Cleavage** Foliation produced in rock by pressure, e.g. slaty cleavage.

**Conglomerate** Sedimentary rock type incorporating rounded transported fragments of an older rock.

**Dalradian** Youngest stratigraphic division of the Precambrian rocks of Scotland and Ireland.

**Diorite** Coarse-grained, intermediate composition igneous rock, formed at depth and composed of intermediate felspars and ferromagnesian minerals.

**Dolerite** Medium-grained, medium depth formed, basic igneous rock.

**Felspars** Important rock-forming silicate minerals.

**Gabbro** Coarse-grained basic igneous rock formed at depth.

**Gastropods** Coiled shelled uni-valved molluscs.

**Graben** Downthrown block between two parallel faults; rift valley.

**Granite** Coarse-grained acid composition igneous rock, formed at depth and essentially composed of quartz, felspar and mica minerals.

**Gneiss** Banded rock formed during regional high-grade metamorphism.

**Inlier** Limited outcrop of older rocks completely surrounded by younger rocks.

**Lamellibranch** Bivalved mollusc with the two valves mirror images of one another, but neither valve is itself symmetrical.

**Larvikite** Coarse-grained syenite consisting largely of anorthoclase felspar showing blue schillerisation.

**Magnetite** Magnetic iron ore mineral.

**Ophiolites** Sequences of basic igneous rocks associated with mid-ocean ridge, sea-floor spreading activity.

**Orogeny** A period of mountain building.

**Outlier** Limited outcrop of younger rocks completely surrounded by older rocks.

**Parting lineation** Parallel laminae due to turbulent eddies close to the surface of the sediment – indicating the direction of the current at the time of deposition.

**Phenocryst** Large crystal set in a groundmass of smaller crystals, see Porphyritic.

**Plagioclase** Sodium or calcium silicate mineral, a felspar.

**Porphyritic** The rock texture where large crystals of one mineral, see phenocryst, are set in a finer groundmass of other minerals.

**Rapakivi texture** Texture in granitic rocks where large orthoclase felspar crystals occur, mantled with smaller soda-rich plagioclase crystals.

**Serpentinite** Rock type formed by metamorphism of an existing ultrabasic rock.

**Sett** Small rectangular paving block made of stone, e.g. granite, used to make a durable road surface.

**Schist** Regionally metamorphosed rock with parallel arrangement (foliation) of the bulk of the constituent minerals.

**Syenite** Coarse-grained intermediate composition igneous rock, containing alkali felspars.

**Travertine** Calcareous deposit formed by hot springs in volcanic regions.

**Xenolith** An inclusion, of a pre-existing rock in an igneous rock.

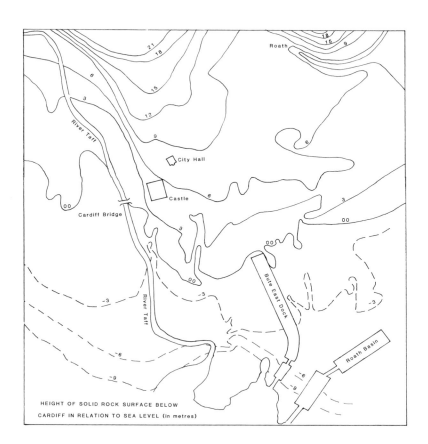

HEIGHT OF SOLID ROCK SURFACE BELOW
CARDIFF IN RELATION TO SEA LEVEL (in metres)